# OPERATION BROTHER'S BROTHER

## Cyril E. Bryant

*With a Foreword by* **BILLY GRAHAM**

PYRAMID BOOKS,      New York

**OPERATION BROTHER'S BROTHER**

A PYRAMID BOOK

Published by arrangement with J.B. Lippincott Company

J.B. Lippincott edition published April 1968
Pyramid edition published November 1969
Second printing, August 1970

Printed in the United States of America

PYRAMID BOOKS are published by Pyramid Publications
A Division of The Walter Reade Organization, Inc.
444 Madison Avenue, New York, New York 10022, U.S.A.

*To Vivian
and All the Other
Sick Children
of the World*

# Contents

# Foreword

This book is the story of one man's determination to do something about the health of the world.

Robert A. Hingson, M.D., learned in an Alabama Sunday school to love the Lord with all his heart, mind and soul. And then he looked seriously at Christ's second great commandment, "Thou shalt love thy neighbor as thyself." For Bob Hingson, a man who was to be trained for medicine, this commandment to love his neighbor meant that he must use his medical skills to bring health, in the name of the Great Physician, to the world's peoples "who live so miserably and die so young."

I know of no other man in our time who has given himself so devotedly to accomplishing this end. He spent twenty years in after-hours work in his laboratory to perfect a tool that would make mass immunization possible. And he then worked with the zeal of an evangelist to sell his convictions on the improvement of world health to medical men and Christian leaders.

Happily, Bob Hingson's enthusiasm (or "magnificent obsession," if we may borrow the title of Lloyd Douglas' famous book) has been a contagious thing. Many hundreds of doctors have heeded his plea that they give their vacations to volunteer medical service overseas. Dr. Hingson himself is the founder and director of "Brother's Brother Foundation"—dedicated to sending volunteer medical teams and armies of youth armed with his jet immunization gun to drive communicable disease from the earth.

This book, then, is a new and thrilling chapter in the story of Christian medicine that began with the miraculous deeds of the Great Physician.

Mr. Bryant, the author, is director of publications for the Baptist World Alliance. He wrote the initial stories of Dr. Hingson's 1958 survey of medical needs of the world and has observed much of the Brother's Brother work first hand. He tells the story with the human-interest flair of a journalist, yet the care and accuracy of a historian.

I hope that the book will be an inspiration to people in all the professions to consider, as Dr. Hingson did, what they can do personally in linking their talents to world needs.

BILLY GRAHAM

*Montreat, North Carolina*

> *I am come that they might have life, and that they might have it more abundantly.*

> John 10:10

# I. A Very Sick World

Her name could have been Maria, or Tasha, or M'bola. There are thousands upon thousands of little girls like her in the world. I'll call her Vivian.

I met Vivian in the Children's Hospital at San José, Costa Rica. She was sitting in bed, her legs crossed to hold her body upright. She looked hopefully at me. I looked wonderingly at her. Her body was that of a one-year-old, but her pretty face, the note of expectancy in her eyes, indicated she was much older, more wise.

Dr. G. Saenz Herrara, the hospital administrator (former vice president of the nation), told me her story. Vivian was a victim of malnutrition. The redness in her normally brown hair bore witness to a lack of the foods that make for a balanced diet. "How old is she?" I asked. "She's six," he said, and then anticipating my next question, "and she weighs seventeen pounds."

Vivian is lucky in a way. She is six and still alive. Fifty-two per cent of the babies born in Costa Rica die within their first five years.

Vivian was one of 525 patients in Hospital de los Niños that day, a hospital with only 460 beds. This meant that 65 beds carried two patients each. The

other patients were there for many diseases of the
tropics, primarily protein deficiencies like Vivian's, or
gastrointestinal diseases, or respiratory ailments.

I was in Costa Rica in company with Dr. Robert A.
Hingson, director of the Brother's Brother Foundation,
a volunteer interfaith group dedicated to the purpose
of linking America's vast medical resources to health
needs in developing countries.

He and a team of other doctors had been invited
there to combat a measles epidemic. Thousands of
new cases were being reported each week, and one of
every eleven cases was ending in death.

We were soon to see—as reports of the Pan American Health Organization had already told us—that
disease was a perennial problem in the Central American republics. Actually I was a little surprised. Newspapers had long reported the tragedy of cholera in
Asia, of smallpox and yellow fever in Africa. But
somehow we Americans felt secure in the mistaken
thought that disease is a stranger to the Western
Hemisphere.

But that illusion did not last long. Across the Nicaraguan border to the north, we found a man whose
face was covered with the blisters of a contagious disease. He was not hospitalized or even isolated from
the population: he was unbelievably, working in Managua's open market, selling produce that his custom-
ers soon would put into their mouths.

In another Nicaraguan town, we met a leper. He
half lay on the sidewalk in front of the hotel facing
Granada's public square, and he braced his shoulders
on the hotel steps. I had thought him to be a beggar,
but he had no cup. Dr. Hingson recognized his problem—legs and feet already blanched and deformed
with leprosy.

Dr. Hingson sought help from the city hospital, then

from both a minister and priest at local rescue homes and from a caretaker at the local cathedral. No institution would agree to take the man in charge, because they feared that the presence of leprosy on their grounds would frighten away other persons. Dr. Hingson, with Wilbur Tucker, a Negro orderly, and Steve Abram, a Jewish medical student on our team, knelt in the gutter and cleaned the man's wounds, applied medicine to the sores, and dressed him in an extra set of clothes offered by Dr. José Amoedo, the Catholic physician on our team—even as the disturbed hotel manager demanded dispersal of the curious crowd.

Smallpox, with frequent outbreaks in South America, is a threat, though generally not endemic in Central America. Leprosy afflicts hundreds from Texas to Chile. The fact that these diseases do occur is evidence that the plagues of past decades have not been obliterated by time; nor are they restricted to the once "far distant" continents of Asia and Africa.

United States health authorities were upset as recently as 1962 when a suspected active case of smallpox was discovered in New York City, brought from Africa to America in only a few hours as a patient crossed the Atlantic by jet aircraft, and when a sick child of a Canadian missionary from Brazil actually reached a New York hotel by taxi.

The role of modern transportation and modern communication in so shrinking the world that one can travel to any city on the globe in twenty-four hours has of course increased the possibility of spread of disease from one continent to another. But it also has fortunately intensified our concern for all the world's peoples.

We know now, more surely than we learned in any Sunday school lesson, that even the most distant peoples of the world are in truth our neighbors.

Dr. Hingson brought this world-neighborliness/ world-health situation into focus by asking me to imagine a visitor who runs onto the front porch of my home. "He is the neighbor boy," Dr. Hingson said, "and he is calling urgently. There is a desperate crisis in his family."

Then he continued: "We leave the luxury of our living room with its color television and stuffed furniture and hurry across our manicured grass lawn. But then, alas, as if through magic, our neighbor's eight-room house and his garden of flowers has vanished.

"In their place is a grass hut. A toothless, tuberculous, blind-from-trachoma grandmother, old at forty-six, stands in the doorway. Your neighbor's wife has just died in childbirth, lying on a straw mat over a mud floor covered with flies. Two of the children are sick with malaria; all have worms; two are coughing following recovery from measles. The year-old baby died last week from malnutrition. None of the children have shoes. Only one has ever been to school. All are physically and physiologically hungry. The father makes nine hundred dollars a year."

Dr. Hingson went on: "Your tendency is to doubt your eyes and your ears and your brain. Yet, this is a true picture of your neighbor if we are to use Christ's interpretation of the word. A billion people in the world—your neighbors—live under the conditions just described."

I came to know the truth of his statement when later we visited the Favela of the Hill of the Bath Tub, overlooking the beautiful city of Rio de Janeiro.

Some say that a third of the population of Rio live as squatters on the sides of the rock-faced mountains that jut upward in the city proper. The majority of these "homes" are shacks made from soft-drink signs or any other scrap material that can be had for free and that will provide shelter from the rain. And the settlements—on land not useful for any other purpose —have the name *favela*, a word peculiar to the squatters' slums of Brazilian mountainsides.

On our trek up the mountainside, some 2,500 feet above the city, we stopped to visit one woman in a lean-to shack the size of four telephone booths. There was a pile of rags on the dirt floor, the bed for this mother and her six children. A little higher up the mountain we found a home with eleven unclad children, from two to fourteen years of age, all with an unmistakable look of hunger in their faces and bodies. Ribs showed through the flesh on their chests, and their bellies were bloated with worms. A sow hog with nine piglets lived in this shack with the human family, the pigs feeding on human excreta. A tenth piglet was already boiling with rice over a slow fire.

Nor were things any better at Guayaquil, Ecuador, where 600,000 people live astride the equator, their lives paralyzed by poverty and human misery. Crawling polio cripples, amputees and children with bloated bellies were in the marketplace, and when we moved to the residential areas we found houses of bamboo cane mounted on shaky foundation poles over black open sewers that spread a stench throughout the neighborhood. Hungry people dug in the black, oily swamps for crayfish or any other available source of protein.

Dr. Hingson believes that much of the world's illness is still unreported. World Health Organization statistics are at the best incomplete and sometimes estimated. In some countries epidemics are so taken for granted that local physicians in the back bush countries never bother to file a formal report with international agencies.

"I have not yet read of the typhoid epidemics in Egypt in nineteen hundred and fifty-eight," he said in illustration. "Yet I walked through the crowded aisles of cots on hot burning sands of the seven thousand people with typhoid fever who were quartered under circus-sized tents as the overflow from the adjacent National and Moslem Hospital. The director of our U. S. Navy Medical Research Unit (NAMRU) at Cairo warned me to take no pictures, since Egypt did not want the world to know of the pestilence. I have heard African ministers of health tell me that smallpox is not a problem in their countries. Yet I have photographed as many as two hundred patients with smallpox in pesthouses ten miles distant. In one of them a missionary nurse told me thirty had died since a physician had visited the place."

These are the people who make up statistical tables. The rows upon rows of figures in a book are monotonous if we see them only as figures—but if we think of world health problems in the light of Dr. Hingson's imaginary family next door—or as these people in the Brazilian *favela* and the Ecuadoran swamp, we sense the magnitude of the problem.

But let us look, anyhow, at the extent of some of the world's major health problems and try in our own minds to imagine every single cipher as a human being—a person like yourself who is ambitious for a happy and fruitful life. And think of the frustration that his lack of health brings to him and to his family.

There are, every year, 100 million new cases of malaria. This figure is approximately equal to half the population of the United States. It includes one of every thirty persons on the earth.

There are 150 million cases of tuberculosis. This one disease kills 50,000 per year in India.

There are many millions of cases of malnutrition, ranging from severe anemia to starvation. This problem gets progressively worse because of increasing populations.

There are 30 million persons suffering from the intestinal diseases of cholera, typhoid, and dysentery.

Another 150 million persons are afflicted with intestinal parasites, amoebae, and worms.

An estimated 40 million people are already blind from trachoma and other diseases of the eyes.

There are 250 million persons ill from bilharzia or snail disease, caused by walking in bare feet through village streams. Two of every five Africans have this disease.

Twenty-five million persons suffer from infectious diseases of the skin—yaws, jungle rot, smallpox and measles.

An estimated 25 million persons have such severe mental apathy they are unable to sustain themselves.

Ten million persons are crippled by leprosy.

These are simply the major diseases. Altogether, about 1 billion persons—one-third of the earth's population—suffer from illness.

Rapidly increasing population has presented another major problem in world health. Vast population gains in India (a current birth rate of 41 per 1,000 population as compared with 21 per 1,000 in the United States) and in all of Latin America (a birth rate of 43.8 per 1,000 in the Middle Americas) have far outdistanced the normal food supply. Deficiency diseases result, and the general population is weakened not only in health but in ability to work and in volume of economic output.

Latin American health authorities report that *la sonda*—the probe—has become the leading cause of death among women between the ages of fifteen and forty-five. *La sonda* is any available pointed metal implement as much as a foot long, usually a knitting needle or a rat-tail comb or a piece of broken automobile aerial, which pregnant women use to rupture the placenta protecting their unborn, unwanted babies. Abortion results—but the crude and unclean probe often causes massive hemorrhages, dangerous infections, and death. Doctors have their own name for *la sonda,* calling it *el carnicero*—the butcher. Probably more than 8 million abortions annually occur in the world's developing nations.

These health problems are understandably a major causative factor in world unrest. Health, happiness, and harmony are essentials for peace, whether in the home, the community, the nation, or the world. Sick fathers are unable to earn a proper living wage for their family, and the family goes without proper food, shelter and clothing. Sick mothers are unable to care properly for their children, and many of their offspring are born with a predisposition to disease.

These poor family situations are reflected in community life, where local governments are financially unable to provide proper schools, proper sanitation, and proper encouragement for economic and health development.

The country in which they live is a have-not nation. And all the moneys that the more prosperous nations pour into these so-called developing nations for commercial advancement can provide only temporary relief—unless and until the health situation is improved.

The World Health Organization has a happy definition, or goal, for world health. Health, they say quite wisely, is more than the absence of disease. Health is, in fact, a person's total physical and mental well-being.

The definition suggests something of what Christ said: "I am come that they might have life, and that they might have it more abundantly."

# II. Bob Hingson's Obsession, and How It Grew

Robert Andrew Hingson, M.D., used a towel to wipe the sweat from his face and arms. Then he began again, vaccinating with machine-gun rapidity the thousands of Nicaraguans who had come to receive smallpox immunization from his highly publicized *pistola de la paz*.

There was no glamour to the occasion, despite the publicity that was being heaped upon him and his team by the newspapers and radio of Managua. This was work, standing hour after hour in humid tropical heat, pumping the lever of a pistol-shaped injector that sprayed vaccine into the arms of men, women, boys and girls who sought protection against the diseases that already had sent many of their friends to the cemetery.

*Pistola de la paz*, translated "the gun of peace," is a jet inoculator that Dr. Hingson and a dozen other technicians have developed over the past few years. It injects vaccine without use of a needle, without danger of infection, and with practically no pain.

Another doctor, with a similar gun, stood opposite Dr. Hingson as the walking line of people moved past. Dr. Hingson's gun injected smallpox vaccine into their left arm; the other doctor simultaneously shot a tuberculosis-leprosy preventative (B.C.G.) into the right arm.

Most people smiled in pleasant surprise when they discovered that *pistola de la paz* lived up to its publicity as a painless injector. One six-year-old boy who had steeled his face for expected pain smiled when he heard the whisp of spray, then turned to his younger brother with the assurance, *"No me duele*—it doesn't hurt."

A nurse stood to the side, busily filling vials with fresh vaccine from picnic-style ice chests. She told me Dr. Hingson had worked with only two interruptions since 8 A.M.; he had stopped briefly at 11, then again for lunch. The afternoon procession had marched by for more than four hours, and the line of waiting people still stretched two abreast three blocks down the street.

The line terminated about sundown, with the mechanical counter registering 5,264 shots for the day. Dr. Hingson, the nurse, and three technicians packed the equipment into boxes, tossed them on the back of a pickup truck, then climbed in themselves for a return to the health center and relaxation.

It was my first day with the team, but forty of its volunteer members had already been ten days on the field. Together they had immunized about 60,000 persons—half their objective for a three-week stay in Nicaragua.

Dr. Hingson had done this sort of thing for five summers—in Asia, Liberia, the Dominican Republic, the Gaza Strip, Honduras, and now in Nicaragua. National health statistics showed the effectiveness of his labors. A smallpox hospital had been closed in Liberia. Lepers were no longer a problem in Honduras.

It was not a mandatory thing for Hingson, because he worked regularly as professor of anesthesia at

Western Reserve University* Medical and Dental
Schools in Cleveland and as director of anesthesia at
University Hospitals. It was in fact a labor of love dur-
ing his vacation time.

"What is it," I asked him at dinner that evening,
"that leads you to give all your spare time, your summer vacations, even your savings accounts to this project that is obviously bigger than any one man can
handle?"

He removed his heavy glasses, and I could see eyes
with the hope and the trust of a boy.

"Jesus gave us two great commandments," he said
without hesitation. "We are to love God, and we are to
love our neighbor as ourselves."

And then he added: "This is all the incentive I need.
Paul's doctrines confuse me, but I know what Jesus
meant when he said to love our neighbors.

"For me personally, it means I must apply my medical knowledge as far as I can reach."

Bob was not preaching. He simply was explaining a
personal conviction.

It seems that from the very day he was born—April
13, 1913—Robert Andrew Hingson was marked for a
career in medicine and a dedication to international
Christian service.

The combination of thirteens could have been an ill
omen for superstitious Southerners if the day had fall-
en on a Friday. But since it was Sunday, the emphasis
in the Bible-belt town of Anniston, Alabama, was on
heavenly things and the happier aspects of mother-
hood and the birth of new life.

* In 1967, Western Reserve University and Cleveland's Case
Institute of Technology merged and as of July 1, 1967, became
Case Western Reserve University. Since most of the events in
this book took place before the merger, "Western Reserve" will
be used in most references.

Robert's father, a buyer and seller of mules in rural Oxford, had driven his expectant wife by horse and buggy along the 3 miles of dirt road to her mother's home in Anniston several days ahead of the anticipated birth. The town physician, possessing the first Model T Ford in town, was on the scene only moments after Grandfather Haynes sounded the announcement of beginning labor.

But Bob came into the world the hard way—by breech delivery. The doctor ordered anesthesia, and Grandmother Haynes dripped chloroform into the improvised inhaler. And therein arose a family argument, repeated so often through the years in a mixture of seriousness and fun that it may have set young Bob on the road to medicine. His mother suffered terribly— and the blame, she felt, belonged to Grandmother Haynes "because she was so stingy with the chloroform."

"They tell me that Mother and Grandmother didn't speak for two days," Hingson now recalls.

Hingson's other memories of those early days as he played in the yard of his home on Oxford's Main Street are a kaleidoscope of health-related patterns. He remembers his first sight of blood, when he stuck a rose thorn into his thumb. He remembers the funeral coaches that regularly passed his home on the way to the cemetery; black horses provided the locomotion and the driver sat on top of the carriage that displayed flower-covered caskets through a glass window. He recalls too his shock, at age five, at seeing a little unclad neighbor girl "who just didn't look quite normal from the waist down."

He was ever aware of the pains and crippling ache of his father's arthritic back. This ailment somehow seemed to make a lot of difference in the things they could do together. He was aware that some of his schoolmates had deformed limbs—a useless arm or a lame leg—caused by an illness they called infantile paralysis. And he became conscious, as the years rolled by, that more little short coffins, the length of his own body, were carried from the Negro side of town than from his own Main Street.

Oxford's church steeples were a second major attraction in young Bob's interesting and sometimes perplexing world. They represented a sort of vertical dimension to life—pointing upward to the blue sky in contrast to the dusty streets on which he played. He sensed that his elders regarded the churches with a sincere respect, and that their regular attendance in church meetings seemed to bring at least a partial holiday to the human suffering and worries of ordinary day-to-day existence.

Bob himself found the church exciting, as his Sunday-school teachers opened a whole new scope of life with immense appeal to his boyish curiosity. He liked the stories of the boy Jesus. He admired the Christ because of his miracles in healing the sick and going about doing good. He memorized the Twenty-third Psalm with its comforting assurance that the Lord was watching His people. He found the assignment to memorize the Ten Commandments a bit boring, however, and was happy that Jesus had compressed these ten Old Testament laws into two great commandments—that he should love the Lord and that he should love his neighbors. His teacher told him that these neighbors included all the people in the world, and that the world reached far, far beyond the mountains that marked the horizon encircling the town of Oxford.

Public school formed a third point of the compass of young Bob's world, but this was not without difficulty. World War I had been a catastrophe to the Oxford schools because of high taxes and its claim on the town's manpower. There was no formal school building for the elementary grades when Bob got to be six. Mother Hingson taught him the alphabet and principles of reading, and Dad Hingson introduced him to arithmetic. He was assigned to the third grade when school did reopen in a reconstructed filling station in 1920.

The Hingsons' own keen interest in religion prompted them to wish a ministerial career for Bob. They enrolled him in public speaking classes at the school and applauded when he won speaking contests one after the other. But Bob soon discovered he liked debate better than oratory, and his ambitions turned more to the law and courtroom arguments than to preaching.

Yet all through grammar and high school he cherished a fondness for medicine. Working with his father in the stables, he learned how to treat the animals if they developed a cold or a fever. He eavesdropped when Oxford's two physicians—who with the elder Hingson comprised the town's school board—came to the Hingson home for a meeting. He learned from them just how sick his playmates might be, and his imagination leaped when they discussed some new aspect of medicine. Many of their words were beyond his vocabulary, but he did understand enough to be interested.

One of the doctors, Mark Williams, brought him two books about Alabama doctors who had made good in the outside world: John Allan Wyeth, the Civil War surgeon, and William Crawford Gorgas, the U. S. Surgeon General who drove malaria and yellow fever from Panama and made possible the building of a canal there. Since both these men were from Alabama, Bob felt a personal identification with them. (He later wrote in a diary: "These books solidified my determination—regardless of the restless depression of the late twenties—to proceed without interruption to a similar place of service to mankind.")

All these impressions came into unexpected focus in Professor T. A. Anderson's mathematics classes in junior high school. Mr. Anderson was seventy-two and would have been a cartoonist's dream. Giant spectacles gave emphasis to the sincerity in his eyes. The gaps between his four remaining teeth seemed only to enhance his benevolent smile. Young Hingson liked him to the point of admiration and was impressed that he inevitably interspersed his arithmetic lessons with Bible reading and discussions of "the wide wide world."

For the first time Bob Hingson was convinced that the world reached far beyond the borders of his county and his state, that the world's peoples were in need, and that he, Bob Hingson, had a responsibility to that world.

Still he debated whether he'd go into the law or medicine. And then he made a bargain with himself. He had won a series of local, county and district high-school debates and was going into the state finals. He decided that if he were good enough to win the state championship, he'd be a lawyer. If not, he'd stick with medicine; which was in reality his first love.

No one knows for sure whether Bob actually tried to win the championship. Anyhow, he came in second and set his life toward medicine.

His convictions for world service were further strengthened as he studied at the University of Alabama (A.B. 1935) and Emory University Medical School (M.D. 1938). In both institutions he worked his way, waiting on tables, firing the furnace, as secretary for the Baptist Student Union, and as orderly and X-ray technician in Druid City and Grady Hospitals. He gained a love for human life as he interned at the U. S. Marine Hospital on Staten Island, New York, and then as an assistant surgeon with the U. S. Public Health Service.

With the outbreak of World War II, he was assigned to the Coast Guard for duty in rescue work and submarine patrol in the North Atlantic. One day in late August 1939 came an emergency message to Captain Joseph Greenspun to move their Coast Guard cutter *Campbell* to Bergen, Norway, to pick up America's fourth-ranking diplomat as a patient. Bob Hingson, the only doctor aboard ship, little dreamed that this might open one of the most significant opportunities in his life.

The patient was Henry W. Morgenthau, Jr., Secretary of the U. S. Treasury. Mr. Morgenthau had been sent to Europe as President Roosevelt's personal representative to try to negotiate with Adolf Hitler in the face of what appeared to be imminent war. Now, only two days before Hitler invaded Poland, Morgenthau, denied even hotel room in Germany in the crescendo of anti-Semitism, sought return to the States. Sea lanes had already been closed in the Skagerrak, and Morgenthau moved across Scandinavia overland to the open sea at Bergen.

His trouble: intense migraine headache. But it was not an ordinary case. Mr. Morgenthau had suffered from migraine throughout his adult life, and the problem was aggravated now by the anxiety of impending war.

"By the time I saw him, he was almost blind from pain and on the verge of collapse," Dr. Hingson wrote in his diary.

The young doctor ran routine tests, then hurried to refer to Dr. William Osler's text, *Principles and Prac-*

*tice of Medicine,* to find the best possible treatment under these circumstances.

Mr. Morgenthau recovered within six hours, but remained Dr. Hingson's personal patient for another week as their ship made its way past mine fields and enemy submarines to a landing in Newfoundland.

"What can I do to repay you?" Morgenthau asked Hingson when he transferred from the ship to a waiting plane in Newfoundland.

"My major desire is to complete my postgraduate education," Hingson replied. "And please mail this letter for me in Washington to my sweetheart, Miss Tobie Dickson." Only a few months later Hingson received, through Surgeon General Thomas Parran, Morgenthau's order for him to proceed for training and study in anesthesia at Mayo Clinic under Dr. John Silas Lundy, the discoverer of pentothal.

Dr. Hingson's training in anesthesiology opened up vast new opportunities. He moved again to the Marine Hospital on Staten Island, 1941–43; to the Lying-In unit of Pennsylvania Hospital in Philadelphia, 1943–45; to the University of Tennessee Medical School in Memphis, 1945–48; and to Johns Hopkins University Hospital in Baltimore, 1948–51. He was meanwhile named an assistant surgeon by the U. S. Public Health Service in 1942, a surgeon in 1943, a senior surgeon in 1950, and then medical director in the U. S. Public Health Service (Reserve) in 1965. He moved in 1951 to Cleveland, on appointment as professor of anesthesiology at Western Reserve University Medical School and director of anesthesia at University Hospitals.

His experiments in anesthesia—perhaps prompted in part by his mother's pains at his own breech birth, but more probably to prevent pain for the first childbirth of his beautiful young wife—won international recognition, at the same time adding to his own international perspective. Concerned about the lack of training centers for anesthesiologists, other than those in the United States and Europe, he persuaded the World Federation of Societies of Anesthesiologists to establish a foundation, which he then organized, for developing training centers in Asia, Africa and South America. (Now he is chairman and president of this foundation that supports medical training for physicians from each of the twenty-six countries in Latin America, with developing plans for Asia and Africa.) He invented a portable anesthesia machine which is small enough to be carried in a doctor's satchel. He developed a method for painless childbirth, continuous caudal analgesia. And he perfected, in collaboration with engineers and manufacturers, a jet gun to vaccinate without the use of a needle.

That Dr. Hingson was gaining respect in all circles was evidenced in 1947 when the U. S. Junior Chamber of Commerce included him on its list of "America's Ten Outstanding Young Men." Another young man on that same list was Richard Nixon.

Bob Hingson, happily married and the father of five children, did not want to leave the peaceful research climate of the Johns Hopkins campus to move to Cleveland. He was happy in the academic life, and he perhaps unconsciously basked in the respect his developments in childbirth anesthesia had brought to him and the university. Twice he rejected the invitation from Western Reserve officials. But when he learned that four mothers had died from aspiration of vomit during anesthesia in childbirth in a single month at University Hospitals, he saw the invitation as a "call."

The visitor soon senses that Hingson has the weight of the world's illnesses on his shoulders—and that he wants to be busy every waking hour. This impression becomes even more concrete as Hingson gives his weekends to speaking engagements across the country and his summer vacations to immunization projects in scattered parts of the world.

At fifty-four years of age, he stands 5 feet 10 inches tall and weighs 180 pounds. His hair lies in neat waves above a high forehead. He leans slightly forward as he walks—appearing to extend himself as fast as possible to the next task on his agenda. He talks with a flow of words that leaves the listener a bit unbelieving.

Every night the weather allows, with his wife and often a beagle named Pepe, he takes a walking cane he inherited from his father and strolls a leisurely 2 miles around Shaker Lake—an expanse of water in front of his home in Cleveland. He explores nature as he walks, and his mind turns to possible solutions to the human and medical problems that confronted him during the day.

It was obvious, on my visit to Dr. Hingson's offices in University Hospitals at Cleveland, that he is one of the most admired individuals on the hospital staff. Some of the admiration obviously comes because of his professional ability. Certainly the seventeen doctors and thirty interns and residents who work under his direction as chief of anesthesiology respect him for his insistence on efficiency and alertness and for his widely recognized leadership in the field of anesthetic medicine.

But another key to the smiles and cheery good mornings that greet him in hospital corridors comes from the fact that Dr. Hingson recognizes all people— charwomen, elevator operators, orderlies, or chiefs of staff—as individuals, and has concern for them as individuals. He asked one lady about her son's recovery from an automobile accident, and he complimented an orderly on his efficiency on a laboratory project.

I asked Dr. Hingson how it is that his administrative duties at Case Western Reserve University allow him to give so much time off the campus to his Brother's Brother projects. He quoted Dr. John Schoff Millis, the university president, as saying that a university faculty has four obligations: to teach, to study, to develop information, and to share information. "My Brother's Brother projects involve me to some extent in all of these aims," Dr. Hingson said.

His enthusiasm is both persuasive and contagious. He dreams big and he talks big. When he speaks of routinely vaccinating 10,000 persons a day, some people find him hard to believe. When he pricks one's conscience to a realization of personal obligation, people either respond to his suggestion or quietly back away to avoid embarrassment. Regardless, he tends to dominate any group or any assembly with his very enthusiasm.

No better test of his leadership can be found than in the fact that his wife, Gussie (nicknamed Tobie), their four sons and a daughter have similarly caught his enthusiasm. All have made intercontinental expeditions with him, sweating under tropical suns to guarantee health to needy people. Indeed, his family shares the academic life with the same vigor and dedication as his. Mrs. Hingson recently achieved her M.S. in Nutrition and regularly teaches in the high-school program for the Cleveland Council on Foreign Affairs. Her service travels in seventy-two countries serve as background for illustrated lectures on the Negroes' progress and identity in the modern world.

The oldest son, Dickson, after finishing at Johns Hopkins, is continuing his career education in the M.D.-Ph.D. program at Harvard Medical School. Roberta, the daughter, has just completed her degree in

the Case Western Reserve University. Andrew has just
graduated from Yale in philosophy. Ralph is a fourth-
year student in international relations at Johns Hopkins. Luke is looking at college from his high school
with a more than usual interest in graduate education
transmitted through this family, truly "advancing by
degrees."

One morning at Granada, the old Nicaraguan national capital founded by the Spanish in 1523, Dr.
Hingson handed me a sheet of mathematical calculations he said he had jotted down during a wakeful
period the night before. He had written, "If one team
of five people can vaccinate 3,000 persons in one day
[as his team had done the day before] that team
would need one million days, or 3,000 years to immunize the world's population." But his calculation went
on to say that 3,000 teams could do the job in one year,
or 36,000 teams could do it in one month. "Imagine,"
he wrote, "a world without polio, tuberculosis, leprosy,
smallpox, measles, diphtheria, whooping cough, lock-
jaw, cholera, influenza and worms."

How much would it cost? He figures the entire
program would require "one-tenth the military personnel and one-fourth the budget of the United States' ex-
penditure for the war in Vietnam." And this cost, he
said, would be ultimately met by savings in the cost of
hospital care for the sick, and in a more stable world
economy sparked by an increased work force and rising standards of living.

But despite his dreams, Bob Hingson is a realist. He
knows that miracles do not happen overnight. He
knows that the wonders that have come to medicine
through the century have resulted from the plodding
and often ridiculed insistence, the tiring trial and
error, of dedicated men. He is not going to sit comfortably in his home at Cleveland Heights and wait for

the world to come around to his position. He will get
out day after day, year after year, to prove the correct-
ness of his theories, the practicality of his dreams.

# III. Hingson the Innovator

Bob Hingson's friends described him as "a man who likes to tinker," and he never denied it. He was born with curiosity, and whenever he saw a problem he usually put both his mind and his fingers to work on the solution.

## The Jet Gun

In Alabama parlance, Hingson, twenty-five, was still green behind the ears when a seaman came to his office in the U. S. Marine Hospital on Staten Island one fall day in 1938. Bob had graduated from Emory University Medical School on June 6, and went immediately—with the M.D. proudly attached to his name— to an internship at the New York medical center.

This seaman held out to Dr. Hingson a badly swollen and painful hand. He did not know what caused the trouble, but the swelling and the pain had developed within a matter of minutes. Hingson was equally perplexed. Nothing in his experience, or in his textbooks, matched the situation. He did remember, however, the saying of a med school teacher that a doctor must sometimes make the best possible guess and then proceed accordingly.

Asking his nurse for a small scalpel, Hingson lanced the seaman's hand and was surprised when almost a tablespoonful of black liquid ran out. He smelled the fluid and rubbed it between his fingers. It had every similarity to crude oil. After cleaning the wound with disinfectant and dressing it, Hingson confessed to the seaman that this was a unique case in his medical experience. The fluid, he said, had every resemblance to oil—but if so, how did it get into the man's hand?

The sailor told him he had been holding a rubber hose through which oil flowed under high pressure—but the oil was inside the hose and he had no idea how it could have gotten into his hand. But as the sailor talked, an idea flashed in Dr. Hingson's mind. Could this, he asked himself, be a case of jet injection?

He reasoned that with oil flowing through the pipe under this extremely heavy pressure, there could have been, exactly where the seaman's hand had grasped it, a minute hole too small to be seen by the eye. This microjet of oil, forcing its way through the tiny orifice at high velocity could have penetrated the hand without leaving any evidence of a puncture. Hingson recalled a footnote in his college textbook that H. Galante, a French doctor, had discovered in 1868 that fluid could be injected in human flesh at high velocity without using a needle. It was conceivably a new method of injection, but it had no positive medical significance because at the time it was far less practicable than the syringe and needle. The idea had popped up again in New York about 1930 and again was laid aside.

But here in the seaman's hand Hingson personally saw the principle at work. The accident had wrought misery to the seaman, yet Hingson sensed that the principle had medical value. Could it not be used for injections and vaccinations in persons afraid of the needle?

For the next several nights, Hingson sketched ideas for a high-pressure injector. He started with a typical hypodermic syringe but removed the needle and left a minute orifice in its place. On the other end, he conceived a cylinder of high air pressure in place of the traditional thumb-operated plunger. A power spring or gas could be compressed, he hoped, in the same way as in a boy's air rifle when it is cocked. And then a trigger would release the plunger into the syringe with such pressure that medicine might be driven through the orifice and into the flesh. His nurse reported her doctor's sketchings to her husband, an engineer. Would it be possible for him to build an injector according to this principle?

Within months, an early working model of the jet inoculator was in Dr. Hingson's hands. The principle was shown to be good, but the gun still needed a great deal of work before it could be an effective medical tool. Many thousand injections, into animals, cadavers, and Hingson himself, lay ahead.

Yet Dr. Hingson believed that here was a beginning of something that could revolutionize the traditional methods of vaccination and other medical injections.

The young engineer immediately sought a patent on his device. And once he got the patient he unfortunately offered it for sale to the highest bidder. Three companies made him offers, and he accepted all three!

Lawsuits resulted from the three-time sale, and the new gun was inevitably and regrettably tied up in court action. The engineer, now deceased, had not sold a complete patent to any of the three and none was able to go ahead with full manufacture. Thus was created a competitive legal deadlock that lasted a decade.

The snafu had an unanticipated advantage to the inquiring Dr. Hingson, however. The basic idea of jet

injection as a public health tool for mass prevention of
disease was his by deduction, and he enlisted the help
of other engineers to build new models for his own use
and experimentation. He had, in effect, an almost ex-
clusive opportunity to experiment with his new tool.
He also had the endorsement of the U. S. Public
Health Service, through the ranks of which he advanced to Medical Director.

Night after night in his spare time he injected dyes
into cadavers, determining just how much pressure
was needed to plant vaccine the desired depth into a
patient's arm. In the long trial-and-error process, he
discovered that a spring mechanism with 125 to 150
pounds pressure would propel the vaccine at a speed
of 700 miles an hour through a micro-orifice of .003
inch to gain the optimum effect as a regulated, controllable injection.

As he grew more sure of the validity of his premise,
Hingson asked his colleague, Dr. Frank H. J. Figge,
professor of anatomy at the University of Maryland, to
test the gun on Hingson's arm, the first live human
flesh to be injected. Hingson gave himself more than
2,000 shots in the next ten years, doing test after test to
learn the optimum measure for the vaccine jet. He fi-
nally settled on the .003-inch orifice—the thinness of a
mosquito's nose and one-thirtieth the size of a conventional hypodermic needle—as the ideal size to pene-
trate the skin with no more pain than a momentary
sting. The injector met all essential requirements for
effective single-shot operation, but still lacked the re-
petitive speed Hingson felt necessary for mass immunization projects. His mind kept hunting for the answer.

It came one day as Hingson watched a painter at
work with a jet spray gun. Why could he not design a
bottle reservoir for vaccine, with a valve to click out
measured amounts with the press of a trigger?

He asked the paint-sprayer manufacturing company to mount the head of his injector onto their power unit, and at the orders of vice presidents Louis and Frank Ziherl, engineering colleagues at the Z and W Manufacturing Corporation in Cleveland built onto the enlarged jet gun a valve that would meter out vaccine in whatever quantities a doctor might order.

Here in truth was a device operating with machine-gun rapidity that could make possible the mass immunization of the world's peoples at the rate of 1,000 per hour per gun.

Why continue to let diseased people suffer, why continue to spend millions of dollars for hospitals and surgery—when preventive medicines applied through the jet inoculator could cut the toll of contagious disease by 90 per cent?

Despite patent conflicts, Dr. Hingson and the Z and W Company were able to manufacture their own model of the jet gun for experimental purposes. Meanwhile, the R. P. Scherer Company in 1946-48, with Hingson, Figge and engineers, had developed a similar gun with similarly happy results.

By 1955, the guns—still not available for public sale—were being used by the U. S. Army at the Walter Reed Hospital in Washington, D. C., by the Navy at its Norfolk, Virginia and Providence, Rhode Island, bases, and by public health officials in mass vaccination projects against poliomyelitis, influenza and smallpox.

However, from 1954 to 1956, Dr. Hingson and his university colleagues had begun the vaccination of preschool children in Cleveland, using the newly discovered Salk poliomyelitis vaccine. The gun injected its vaccine as fast as the children could walk past the doctor—and few of the children so much as whimpered. In fact, in University Hospital during a polio epidemic, when two lines of small children were marching in competing lines, inoculated by needle on one line and the experimental jet on the other, one little boy crawled under a table to leave the squalling needle line and march through the no-pain jet line.

In 1956, Cleveland post-office employees asked Dr. Hingson to give poliomyelitis and influenza vaccines to them and their families. The "patients" gathered on designated nights, and thousands received protection free, as study patients, within the time they usually spent singly waiting their turn in doctor's offices. Eighty-five hundred of these workers and their families received a total of 89,730 immunizations between 1956 and 1961. It proved conclusively to Hingson that the jet gun could do what he dreamed of in mass immunization programs.

But here, as in many other instances, Dr. Hingson ran counter to the traditions of other medical men. Mass immunization held the peril of infection, they said, and there also were doubtless some persons in the walking lines who should have been screened by means of their medical history before being given shots to which they might be allergic. But the records over a six-year period validated the wisdom of Hingson's theories.

The jet inoculator was first called a gun of peace in Burma in 1958. A wide-eyed boy watched Drs. Hingson, John G. P. Cleland and Blanchard Antes vaccinate one person after another with such rapidity that he exclaimed "Man, that's some gun." His sister responded, "But it's not a bad gun; it's a peace gun."

Dr. Hingson adopted the name, believing that if the gun could lead to the death of disease it was truly a gun of peace.

The jet guns were to be further demonstrated and tested in a round-the-world tour in 1958 and in a mass

immunization campaign in Liberia in 1962. Those
stories are told in later chapters.

## Painless Childbirth

Dr. Hingson returned to the U. S. Marine Hospital
on Staten Island in 1941, after a year of training in anesthesia at Mayo Clinic. But now he was director of
anesthesia, not an intern, and his responsibility covered all pain-killing aspects of the hospital's 7,000
operations per year.

Surgery cases usually could be scheduled for day-
light hours, but maternity cases were a different matter. Night after night he found himself and Dr. W. B.
Edwards, obstetrician, attending childbirth for the
wives of servicemen. It was a unique assignment in a
hospital that generally served only men patients, and
the two doctors took a lot of razzing whenever a mother in the pains of labor disturbed the usual hospital
quiet.

One evening in late 1941, an expectant mother came
into the labor room in unusually severe pain—the kind
that Dr. Hingson describes as the "O help me Jesus"
stage of childbirth suffering. He discovered that the
woman's medical history of heart failure and allergies
refuted the wisdom of using any known form of anesthesia.

Hurriedly he ran through his mind the other possibilities open for reducing the woman's pain. He knew
that French doctors Cathelin, a urologist, and Sicard,
a neurologist, had developed independently a principle of caudal (tailbone) anesthesia in 1901. Three
other doctors, Van Gaza, Läewen and Schlimpert, also
had experimented with it around 1920 in Germany.

The principle itself was basically simple, but its application difficult because it-called for a needle injec-

tion into the sacral hiatus about two inches deep in the body. Dr. Cathelin had found that anesthetic thus introduced into the peridural space behind the spinal column would deaden nerve endings throughout the middle part of the body. Yet, because anesthesia did not enter the spinal column itself, the danger of paralysis, headache and unconsciousness was reduced to a minimum. (For some reason, Dr. Cathelin never used the method in obstetrics.)

It was this rare alternative which Dr. Hingson chose for the suffering mother at Marine Hospital in 1941. Carefully, slowly, he inserted a needle in search of the small opening. In less than ten minutes, the woman was resting comfortably. Her heart failure cleared. Pain returned about two hours later, and he repeated the process. Fortunately the woman delivered her child before effects of the second injection wore off.

As they discussed the case together the next morning, Dr. Edwards jestingly asked Dr. Hingson what he would have done if the woman had stayed in labor all night. Certainly one could not inject shot after shot into the same tiny opening. Dr. Hingson replied, in similar humor, "I guess I would have inserted a needle tied to a tube and run the other end down the hall to my bedroom. Then anytime she screamed I could have sent her a little more anesthesia."

Such a system, Dr. Hingson decided, should be called "continuous caudal analgesia."

Fortunately, Dr. Hingson did not let the idea die with that conversation. He and his wife and Dr. and Mrs. Edwards searched the medical books, and he made repeated visits to the hospital's anatomy lab to learn all he could about the caudal cavity into which medicine had to be injected if this method was to be practical.

Scratching his designs on paper, he asked a medical

manufacturer, Oscar Schwidetzky, to prepare a flexible hollow needle long enough to reach the two inches to the sacral hiatus and large enough to carry a catheter. Both Dr. Edwards and Dr. Hingson were about to become fathers, and each, in the protective devotion of physicians and husbands, sought perfection through this new technique for those they loved most. And they realized early that their technique brought both safety and relief of pain never before achieved.

Dr. Hingson's system was much the same as the joke he had made with Dr. Edwards. The needle is injected into the sacral hiatus. Once the end of the catheter is in place through the opening, the needle itself is removed by pulling it over, like a sleeve, the length of the tube. The loose end of the tube is brought over the woman's shoulder and pinned to her gown. Repeated shots of an anesthesia can thus be injected without additional needle punctures. It is this feature that made Dr. Hingson's technique practical and called for use of the word "continuous" in the name.

Good news soon spreads, and though Dr. Hingson and Dr. Edwards still considered their technique in the experimental stage, rumors of the discovery of painless childbirth found its way to the American Medical Association offices in Chicago. From there, Dr. Morris Fishbein, then editor of the *Journal of the American Medical Association,* phoned Dr. Hingson.

"I hear that you have a system of painless childbirth," he said. Dr. Hingson replied that he and Dr. Edwards were experimenting with a process that gave a promise of success.

When the highly respected Fishbein identified himself, Dr. Hingson thought some friend was pulling a prank. He declined therefore to talk more about it to the stranger. The caller closed the conversation with the promise that he would fly to New York to see things for himself.

Two days later, Dr. Fishbein and his wife arrived. Dr. Hingson was relieved to know he had not been victim of a practical joker. And he sensed even more strongly the importance of the technique he was developing.

Dr. Fishbein slipped a hospital coat over his clothes, and all day he watched with amazement as one mother after another gave birth without pain. Even more amazing, muscle movement continued normal for expulsion of the child, and the mother stayed fully conscious, talking with the doctors and exclaiming her joy when she saw her baby for the first time. The children were born breathing—not requiring a spank on their behinds—because caudal anesthesia did not anesthetize the newborn!

Dr. Fishbein wrote the story for his *A.M.A. Journal* and, aware of the public interest in a discovery that could bring relief to every future mother, he sent a copy also to *Reader's Digest*. The *Digest* printed the story in April 1943, before its publication in the *Journal*. Dr. Hingson was victim for the first time of criticism that has followed him much of his professional career—being a publicity seeker. "Why did he give the story to the *Digest* before it was published in medical journals?" critical colleagues asked.

When the *Journal* carried the story a few months later, doctors everywhere looked hopefully at it. Dr. Hingson was commissioned by the Public Health Service to tour across America, speaking in medical schools and at regional academies of medicine to demonstrate the technique and train doctors in its use.

Now, in 1968, more than 8 million mothers in the United States alone have been blessed by the use of the continuous caudal technique. Dr. Hingson himself has provided this relief to 15,000.

I was privileged to watch Dr. Hingson bring peace to one young mother at McDonald House, the maternity division of University Hospital in Cleveland. The patient, a Mrs. Thompson, was eighteen, about to bear her first child. Dr. Hingson and I could hear her cries as we walked hurriedly down the hall to her room. "I can't stand it, doctor, I just can't stand it," she said.

Dr. Hingson's personality had changed in a minute from that of busy executive to that of a small-town doctor interested only in the welfare of the patient in front of him. He called her by name and told her he could stop the pain completely. She looked at him in disbelief; not even her wish for relief could persuade her that relief was possible.

She obeyed his instruction to roll over on her side. "Now I am going to give you a local anesthetic so that you will not feel the larger needle we will be using in a minute," he said. "This needle prick will be the last pain you will feel."

Gently he injected an anesthetic into the mid-lowermost portion of her back. Then he proceeded immediately to take a larger needle from a caudal anesthesia kit and probe cautiously and gently for the sacral opening. He had done it so many times that the needle went directly to its mark. "I have never seen it done so easily," whispered a resident doctor who was observing.

Dr. Hingson turned to the young medic and me to explain that he now would test to make sure the needle had found its mark. He applied a plunger device into the end of the needle. "If I have made a mistake and gone into the spinal sac, clear fluid can be aspirated, or if I have missed my mark entirely, pressure from inside will force this plunger back out," he explained.

But the plunger remained steady. "This means I am into the canal, as I intended," he said.

Next—and it all happened faster than one can write it—he removed the plunger and slipped a catheter tube through the hollow needle. Removing the needle, but leaving the tube, he used a syringe to inject a test dose, and then 10 cc. of anesthetic into the catheter's open end.

His fingers marched up her abdomen to indicate the movement of the anesthetic's deadening action inch by inch up the patient's muscle system. "Dr. John Cleland of Oregon discovered that the eleventh and twelfth abdominal nerves are the key to pain control in child-birth," he explained. "Within another minute the medicine will be fully effective."

"How do you feel now?" he asked the patient. The answer was obvious because she had begun to smile. "I don't hurt at all," she said.

"But you are having a pain right now because I can see your womb contracting," he told her. Then they talked about her husband's work, and her hope that the child would be a girl. "I think you're wrong," Dr. Hingson joked. "This baby will play football someday with the Cleveland Browns."

Dr. Hingson and I visited other areas of McDonald House, and came back to Mrs. Thompson's room some ninety minutes after we had left. She was beginning to feel slight pain, and he instructed the doctor in charge to inject another 10 cc. of anesthetic. Her pain was gone again.

"She's ready to deliver," the doctor said. Nurses helped her lift herself to a cart and rolled her into the delivery room.

Twenty minutes later, an 8-pound, 10-ounce boy was delivered, crying lustily even as the doctor severed the umbilical cord. "See, I told you that he was

going to play for the Cleveland Browns," Dr. Hingson
said. "Is he all right?" the mother asked. "A really fine
and healthy baby," said the obstetrician. "Oh, thank
you, God," Mrs. Thompson exclaimed. And we all
laughed with her in her joy.

Doubtless we were sharing the same enthusiastic
approval noted by Dr. J. P. Greenhill, the Chicago
gynecologist who wrote: "Properly performed, this is
the most effective method for relief of pain in childbirth today."

### The Portable Resuscitator

Doctors run into the problem time and again! Heart
attack and asthma victims on submarines—desperately
in need of oxygen. A wounded man on the street, the
breath knocked out of him—desperately in need of oxygen. In some cases, the patient recovers; in many
others he dies.

Hingson first faced the dilemma in his work with
the Navy. Submarines simply cannot be equipped
with the elaborate conduits and the large tanks of oxygen on which hospitals rely so heavily. He saw the
problem also in mission hospitals and clinics in Africa,
Asia, and Latin America. Doctors were operating
without benefit of anesthesia, patients were fighting
for their lives without the advantage of oxygen.

Hingson, the tinkerer, wished for a portable device
to perform these essential medical tasks. Something in-
expensive enough that every physician could afford it.
Something simple enough that even a layman could
operate it. Something small enough to fit into a doctor's satchel or a businessman's briefcase.

He sketched and helped build a three-section unit:
an expandable breathing bag, a plastic face mask, and
receptacles for thumb-sized cylinders. Each of the

cylinders, 2½ inches long, was in fact a minia-
ture 3-liter oxygen tank, so carefully engineered that a
twist of the cylinder would break the seal, open the
valve and inflate the breathing bag. (His partners in
design: the Jugoslav immigrant brothers Frank and
Louis Ziherl and Hungarian engineer Kish. "It's team-
work," he insisted. "No one works alone and suc-
ceeds.")

The patient thus breathes the oxygen whenever the
mask is held over his face. A single cylinder is adequate for three to five minutes of breathing, and additional cylinders can be screwed into place as needed.

The complete device, when deflated, was scarcely
larger than a stethoscope, and it weighed less than 2
pounds. Here was something every doctor could carry
in his medical bag—for emergency use whenever
needed. Persons with heart disease are encouraged to
carry the inhaler and spare oxygen cylinders in their
briefcases—for use in emergency. Dr. Hingson presented a unit to President Eisenhower after the President's heart attack in 1953. Dr. Howard M. Snyder,
the President's physician, told Hingson later that the
unit traveled with the President everywhere he went
and that it contributed to the saving of Mr. Eisenhower's life in a second emergency illness.

Dr. Hingson took the resuscitator with him to the
American Medical Assocation section on anesthesia in
1957 and demonstrated how it could be used also for
administration of anesthetic gases. The placement of
two or four receptacles for gases allowed the doctor to
mix anesthesia with oxygen for safe analgesia. It doubled the machine's usefulness to the general practitioner who might need it for emergency use in reducing fractures, lancing abscesses and stitching wounds.
(The machine is now generally referred to as "the

Western Reserve University gas machine," although there are more technical names for varying models.)

When Dr. Hingson visited the hospital of the Maryknoll Sisters at Pusan, Korea, in 1958, he left with them both oxygen-supplied and mouth-to-mouth resuscitators—the latter a pipe-type gadget that allows a separation between the mouths of victim and rescuer. A year later Sister Mary Lois reported, "About the Johnson & Johnson mouth-to-mouth resuscitators—indispensable! Gas cylinders we may not be able to get but 'hot air' that we've got! You can not imagine the number of times that clean little device has saved a life in the clinic, Doctor . . . the most untrained can handle it successfully."

She then told of a man who had recently been brought in in a coma, with signs of hemorrhage, who went into respiratory arrest while she was trying to make a diagnosis and institute treatment. After the first few minutes of keeping him alive with the resuscitator, during which his sixteen-year-old son was frantically asking if he could help, she said, "Yes, you can breathe for your father." The boy followed her "breathe-in" and "breathe-out" directions with the resuscitator until, thirty-five minutes later, his father's own lungs took over. "We could use about five or six more," she wrote, "and . . . cover all the vital spots of this . . . conglomeration of clinic buildings. . . . I'd hate to think how many of us would even think of such a simple solution if you had not come. . . ."

Dentists have discovered the gas machine's anesthesia capabilities for oral surgery. I saw its usefulness and great flexibility during a dental clinic at Cleveland's Metropolitan Hospital, where Dr. Hingson and Dr. Anthony J. Tomaro, professor of dental surgery at Case Western Reserve, contribute their time every Tuesday morning to service cases.

None of the patients were free of contraindications. Many were anemic. Others were habitual smokers, others had an allergic cough. Dr. Hingson talked personally with each patient and regulated the mixture of anesthesia and oxygen for the benefit of those whose lungs and blood were not normal.

The flexibility of the portable machines was further evident as Dr. Hingson gauged the amount of anesthesia also to fit the length of time Dr. Tomaro expected to be working in the mouth. People with only one or two teeth to be extracted slept less than two minutes. Yet one woman slept twelve minutes while the dentist extracted ten teeth.

Dr. Hingson discussed each case with his audience of students, explaining his operational procedures and his reasons for each step or deviation from normal. He was definitely the dominant person in the room, and I could not help but chuckle when a student half whispered, "Dr. Hingson is such a showman you'd think he was more important than the dentist." And then on second thought, this student who is studying anesthesia himself added: "Actually he *is* more important. A dentist never kills a patient. The patient's life rests in the hands of the anesthetist."

But the anesthetic mortality record is not bad. Dr. Hingson and his colleagues have handled more than 40,000 cases in their years at the dental clinic. There has been only one death—one out of 40,000.

## Negro Deaths

Dr. Hingson's perpetual curiosity leads him to study statistical charts and make mental notes of phenomena that may be hidden in the mass of figures. In the mid-1940's he became disturbed over figures showing that two and one-half to four times as many Negroes as whites die under anesthesia. He discovered, for instance, that of the 670,000 Negro women giving birth to their first child in a single year, 1956, 1,000 mothers and 25,000 babies did not survive the anesthetic. He learned too that of a million Negroes having surgery that same year, more than 1,000 died either under anesthetic or within six hours.

The doctor believed that there must be some reason for this racial disparity—that some secret existed that could save the lives of most of these 27,000 persons.

He looked at his own hospital experience to discover that 5,000 Negro mothers had been delivered at University Hospitals in a three-year period without a single mortality. And he asked himself what made the difference.

Sometimes a complicated problem is easier to solve than a simple one. And one factor of the answer that Dr. Hingson found was a thing of absolute simplicity.

Anesthetists have habitually supplemented their various mechanical tests with a visual observation of a patient's skin color. If the flesh of a white patient begins to turn blue, he knows that the patient needs more oxygen. He simply turns a knob to increase the flow of oxygen into the mixture of gases, and skin color returns to normal.

But such a visual test is not possible on black skins! Furthermore, collapsed veins under pigmented skin during shock cannot be entered easily or rapidly for transfusion.

Dr. Hingson explained that while an anesthetic mixed with 20 percent oxygen is routinely sufficient, this does not leave a sufficient margin of safety for the Negro. He recommended that the routine mixture be increased to 40 per cent for those patients with the darkest skins.

Again, the Western Reserve University gas machine

came into play. Dr Hingson and his associates found they had better manipulation of mixtures through the portable machine's hand operation than in the hospital's flowmeters. And with this additional tool, his research continued.

Not all the trouble is with routine anesthetic procedures, he decided. Part of it comes from the Negro's personal insecurity, his socio-economic status in an America that has until the past decade been essentially dominated by whites. "History has set the stage," he asserted, "for a melancholia associated with fear, distrust and delayed medical care. All these have greatly increased the rate of morbidity and mortality among the Negro people."

He pointed also to "slums of northern cities, the charity wards of city hospitals, the unpainted shanties of southern America—without plumbing." These too contribute to the Negro's health problem.

Dr. Hingson recorded his findings in medical journals, listing the measures which he believed would immediately reduce mortality rates among Negroes. Nineteen sixty-six brought the first encouraging relative reduction in Negro death rates in three centuries.

# IV. A Dream Is Launched

The beginning of Brother's Brother was a "happening." It was not planned in the usual sense. Sure enough, there was a dream in the mind of Robert Hingson and doubtless in the minds of uncounted scores of others who hoped for some miracle that would free the world of disease. But no one knew how to bring that dream to reality.

Hingson had both the dream and the tool. He believed that the jet gun could immunize hundreds and thousands of persons as fast as they walked past its nozzle.

He was also aware, however, of the realities of the world around him. He knew that doctors and other medical people were occupied with their own practices and the business of making a living for their families. He knew that vaccines are terribly expensive, and that even the fortunes of a Rockefeller could not underwrite the full cost. He knew too of the thousands of miles between the resources in America and the tragic needs in Latin America, in Asia, and in Africa. And he knew still further that even if the resources could be made available, there was not the organizational know-how or motivation in many foreign lands to bring to reality the dream in his mind.

But still the dream persisted.

Bob Hingson's study of medicine and his long hours in the laboratory had not diminished his speaking ability. He remembered his successes as a youth—back in those days when finding something to talk about was three-fourths of the problem of making a declamation. And now, without a doubt, he had something important to say. He had a conviction and he had the facts to back up his arguments.

Week after week, month after month, he boarded planes out of Cleveland Airport to tell his story to all audiences that would listen.

He made himself available for appearances in college campus seminars, especially the religious-emphasis-week programs when youth like to dream of noble accomplishments. He spoke to gatherings of medical men, to describe the jet gun and tell of its potential in mass immunization. He appealed also to church groups, believing that here he would find people motivated by their own experiences with the Great Physician.

"God has no favored people, no favored nation, no favored race," he told the Laymen's Leadership Institute at Louisville, Kentucky, in January 1957.* "We who love God must love all the world's peoples. And while all people are equal in the sight of God, they are grossly unequal in health, in available nutrition, in life expectancy. It is just as imperative for America's affluent people to minister to . . . the leper in Africa as it was for the traveler to give aid to the wounded man in Jesus' story of the Good Samaritan."

He spoke of his experiences in the operating room when, he said, he was a partner with Jesus in bringing peace to pain-wracked bodies and in helping restore

* See Appendix 2.

health to the sick. He spoke of the terrific need for the healing hand of the Great Physician in many parts of the world. And he told the men that the answer to these problems rested in their own willingness to give of themselves; in fact to love their neighbors as themselves.

Dr. Hingson's obvious sincerity added emphasis to his words. There was a stirring among the audience as he added a plea that medical doctors and technicians volunteer their time, knowledge and resources to minister to their suffering brethren in developing nations.

W. Maxey Jarman, a Baptist deacon from Nashville, Tennessee, and chairman of the board of the multi-million-dollar Genesco Corporation, sensed that Hingson's plea was one of merit. As soon as the session adjourned he quietly walked over to his friend Robert S. Denny, associate secretary of the Baptist World Alliance. He asked Denny what he knew of Hingson, and of Denny's reaction to the validity of the Hingson appeal. He mentioned that the Jarman Trust, a benevolent fund left in his father's will, might be willing to invest in an exploration of some of the doctor's proposals.

Denny commended Hingson as a man of both ability and high motivation, and proposed that Jarman, Hingson and himself get together for breakfast the next day.

Jarman frankly told Hingson that it seemed he was reaching for the moon. There was no disrespect for the worthiness of Hingson's goals nor of his motivation. But he wanted to know how these goals could be attained. Half the morning rushed by as the three men brainstormed, first envisioning the needs and objectives and then placing these objectives against reality.

Jarman then talked about his direction of the Jarman Trust, and the Trust's provisions for advancement of Christian causes around the world. He offered to make a gift to the Baptist World Alliance for whatever amount seemed reasonable and necessary to underwrite a survey trip to determine medical needs in Asia and Africa.

Dr. Hingson remembers the occasion as one in which Jarman tossed a challenge at him: "If you can find five doctors who will leave their practice for four months to do this job, I'll put the gas in your plane."

Dr. Hingson accepted the challenge—then wondered if he could meet his end of the bargain. It is not easy for a doctor to leave his practice, for this sometimes leaves patients unattended and abruptly cuts off income while family costs and much operational overhead continue. Dr. Hingson demanded also, in his own planning, that the men to go must be among the best in their field. The tour was a major undertaking with tremendous possibilities. There would be no room for mediocrity.

The first man on Hingson's list was John G. P. Cleland, M.D., a surgeon and obstetrician of Oregon City, Oregon. For two decades Dr. Hingson had intimately known Cleland and the quality of his research at McGill University in Montreal as they exchanged research notes about the principles of painless childbirth. Dr. Cleland had engaged in major research on birth pains since 1927 and was the first to delineate the nerve pathways of the uterus. Dr. Hingson was adapting the principles of caudal anesthesia to these anatomical discoveries. Dr. Cleland had written, in a meticulous paper of forty-eight pages, the results of several years' study on the mechanisms of the specific pains a woman suffers in childbirth and submitted it to medical journals. Editors for practical reasons required a condensation to twelve pages. Dr. Hingson properly re-expanded this important subject and was co-author of the first book ever written on obstetric anesthesia.

It was within the scope of this friendly and professional relationship that Dr. Hingson decided he wanted John Cleland on the survey team. The decision came to Hingson with clarity during the night, and he placed a long distance telephone call to Cleland early the next morning.

He had not remembered the time difference between Cleveland, in the Eastern Standard Time zone, and Oregon City, with Pacific Time. It was six o'clock on a Sunday morning, therefore, when Dr. Cleland's telephone aroused him from sleep.

Dr. Hingson enthusiastically told his story and urged Cleland to come along on the survey mission. The Oregon doctor listened for twenty minutes, with only an occasional question to satisfy his mind on specific details.

"Who was that?" Dr. Cleland's wife asked sleepily.

"It was Bob Hingson in Cleveland."

"What did he want?"

"He wanted me to go around the world with him."

"And what did you say?"

"I told him I would go."

A few weeks later Cleland and Hingson met in Washington, D.C., as invited consultants to the 1958 White House Conference on the employment of the physically and mentally handicapped. They talked further of their plans. They wanted to make the trip in the summer of 1958. But they realized that the time was drawing short, and still only two men—themselves—were available.

They decided it was a matter too big for them to handle alone. And they prayed together in their hotel room.

When they stopped praying, they came up with the

name of Eugene H. Dibble. Dr. Dibble was, and is, one of America's most highly respected Negro physicians. He has been director of the John A. Andrew Memorial Hospital at Tuskegee, Alabama, since 1946, and has contributed greatly to the medical welfare of mankind. The prenatal care clinics he organized have saved hundreds in Alabama. He believed with his hero, Booker T. Washington, that the secret of solving a sociological problem is found in the solution of the problems of the man farthest down.

Dr. Hingson telephoned Alabama. Dr. Dibble promised to think about it; later, when told that his fellow Southerners had nominated him to join the first interracial, interfaith, interdisciplinary team to leave the United States on a mercy mission, he said yes.

Many other names were suggested. Some, including Dr. Stanley Olsoi of the Baylor University Medical School, wanted badly to go but could not work the time into their schedule.

Two others, both suggested by Mr. Denny of the Baptist World Alliance, completed the group of five mentioned in Mr. Jarman's bargain. They were Dr. Charles Black, a surgeon of Shreveport, Louisiana, with special interest in tuberculosis control, and Dr. Gabe Payne, a pediatrician of Hopkinsville, Kentucky, who was personally concerned with the health and future of millions of children around the globe.

Drs. Dibble, Cleland, Payne and Hingson made arrangements to take their wives—all trained in hospital skills—at their own expense. Dr. Cleland's daughter, Molly, an expert student in French, volunteered to go as interpreter and secretary. Still others helped swell the party: Miss Mary Hebe Degler, a nurse-anesthetist connected with Western Reserve hospitals who had worked with Dr. Hingson since 1942; Edward C. Dixon, president of Continental Hospital Industries;

James C. Lawson, sales manager of the Z and W Manufacturing Corporation, makers of one model of jet inoculator, the Press-o-jet, and the Western Reserve gas machine; Mrs. Josephine Robertson, staff writer for the Cleveland *Plain Dealer;* and George Pitkin, a photographer. Each made his own financial arrangements.

Only days before the team was to leave, Dr. Blanchard Antes, a gentle sixty-three-year-old Canton, Ohio, gynecologist, read in his morning newspaper of the plans. He was a Methodist layman who had nourished in his own mind some of the hopes Dr. Hingson was expressing for world health. He had in fact heard Dr. Hingson's 1957 address at the Laymen's Leadership Institute, but he did not know of plans for the survey trip until he read Josephine Robertson's announcement of it.

Dr. Antes is not a man usually given to impulse, but he reached for his phone and asked Dr. Hingson for an appointment the next day. He did not tell of the purpose of his visit, because his hopes were still in the stage of inquiry. Dr. Hingson said he could see him at 11:30.

The Hingson day was busy. He reached his office from surgery a few minutes late, apologized to Dr. Antes for his tardiness, visited briefly and then urged his visitor to join him and some others for a luncheon at a café just off campus. The Canton doctor went along, listening as Cleveland members of the tour discussed their plans. Then as the luncheon broke up, Dr. Antes walked with Dr. Hingson to his car.

"I put my hand on his arm and told him simply and definitely, 'I am going with you,'" Dr. Antes recalls.

Dr. Hingson told him he would be welcome, but that all plans had already been made. There was no Jarman Trust money to underwrite his travel costs. It was doubtful that airplane space could be secured at this late date. Passports and visas also would be necessary.

Dr. Antes volunteered that he would take care of all this. Dr. Hingson, convinced of Dr. Antes' sincerity, shook his hand firmly. They agreed that since Dr. Antes and his wife, a dietician, could not be ready for departure from San Francisco on July 3, they should plan to join the tour two weeks later in Manila.

This sudden decision by Dr. Antes is one of the significant parts of the Brother's Brother story. Here was a man of conviction, approaching retirement age, launching out on faith and his own resources to do what he believed the Lord wanted him to do. He has since traveled with Dr. Hingson on every major project, leading some on his own. Dr. Hingson pays him this tribute: "Dr. Antes, the right arm of our Foundation, has the energy at seventy of many at forty, the dedication at the highest pinnacle when the timberline of convention is reached; his faith moves the mountains of obstruction; his love for the sick brings the Kingdom of God earthward."

# V. Global Medical Mission Survey

Members of the survey team picked the annual meeting of the American Medical Association in San Francisco, in late June 1958, as the appropriate point and time for departure. They would converse with colleagues on the latest in modern medicine. Then by trans-Pacific clipper they would fly to points of the world desperately in need of these new techniques.

Dr. Hingson called the team together for a briefing session at the Mark Hopkins Hotel the day before their scheduled departure. They spent five hours in conference, learning something of one another and each confiding his own hopes for the mission. It was really a time of wonder, for though many of the team members had traveled abroad none had undertaken anything as strenuous as the trip Dr. Hingson outlined.

"We will go into the slums and the jungles," Dr. Hingson said. "We will go through long hours of fatiguing work.

"Some of us may not get back. Some of us may get sick and may have to be left behind. Our job will be to go on, to reach our objective, once we have put our hands to the plow."

And then he added: "If any of you think your decision was unwise, now is the time to withdraw."

After a moment for them to think over his abrupt invitation for quitters, he went on: "We will have the opportunity to put the principles of Christianity into practice in the uttermost parts of the earth. We will have the wonderful opportunity of rendering a service and of interpreting both Christianity and America to peoples in far distant lands."

The team also had a letter from Mr. Denny, who could not be with them at San Francisco because he was, that same week, leading a Baptist Youth World Conference in Toronto. The letter reminded them that the trip would not be all pleasure, that heat, travel problems, physical exhaustion would be ever-constant companions. "Be tolerant of the beliefs of others and where indicated take off your shoes. It is somebody's holy ground."

He urged them to take a positive look at themselves and their projects despite these difficulties. "Wait to complain, wait to criticize, wait to condemn," he wrote. "Hurry to praise. Your purpose is to learn as well as to teach."

The team left San Francisco by Pan American Airways and arrived in Honolulu later the same day. Missionaries, alerted by correspondence from the Baptist World Alliance, met their plane and dropped Hawaiian leis over their shoulders.

It was a happy beginning, in contrast to the appalling conditions that lay ahead. An hour-by-hour report of the hundred days of travel is not possible in the space of this chapter, nor is it necessary. Let us simply look briefly at the highlights of each stop, and then at the recommendations of the medical men:

*Honolulu, Hawaii*—Doctors viewed rows of empty beds when they visited a leper colony on Molokai Island, learning that new medicines can be expected to eradicate the once dreaded disease from Hawaii by 1981. They left with Hawaiian doctors a new plastic airway designed by Dr. Hingson to aid mouth-to-mouth resuscitation. Dr. Hingson explained that mouth-to-mouth resuscitation to restore breathing was first used by Elisha, as recorded in II Kings 4.

*Tokyo, Japan*—More than 1,000 Japanese doctors, including their personal friends and former students Drs. Takeuchi, Okawa, Yammamura and Fugimoto, heard lectures by members of the team in Kyoto, Osaka and Tokyo. Dr. Cleland demonstrated a new method of spinal anesthesia at the University of Tokyo, at the Baptist hospital in Kyoto, and in the Presbyterian Hospital in Osaka. Impressed by the excellence of Japanese hospitals, Dr. Payne asked Dr. Jim Satterwhite why a medical mission hospital had been set up in the modern city of Kyoto. Dr. Satterwhite replied: "We are here for only one reason. We have only one excuse for existing, and that is to show Christian love through medical care."

*Pusan, Korea*—The team observed tragic sanitary conditions in this seaport city with a population of more than 1 million. Happily, they found staff members of the Baptist hospital working in cooperation with a Catholic hospital operated by the Maryknoll sisters, each institution sharing with the other their facilities for health care. Mrs. Beatrice Cleland, R.N., who before her marriage was superintendent of the Montreal Civic Hospital and formerly Surgical Supervisor of the Royal Victoria Hospital, was particularly distressed by the fact that the cold wet climate would not permit the drying of hospital linens out of doors. The Maryknoll Sisters had devised their own primitive system of stretching laundered linens across 6-foot-wide baskets under which a small fire burned.

*Hong Kong*—An estimated 100,000 refugees sleeping in the streets moved the team to compassion. Similar congestion existed at Kwong Wah Hospital, where 21,000 babies are delivered each year and mothers lie three and four in a bed. Dr. S. G. Rankin and his limited staff treat 500 patients a day in the Baptist clinic. "Help us if you can," Dr. Rankin pleaded. "Best, pray for us."

*Manila, Philippines*—Inflation that makes a glass of orange juice cost an American dollar, coupled with cheap labor that furnishes taxi rides for less than a dime, provides a perfect setting for malnutrition and disease. Local doctors estimated that more than 90 per cent of the people have intestinal parasites. Medical services are handicapped by a lack of laboratory facilities and the inability of most patients to pay for even the simplest prescribed medicines.

*Rangoon, Burma*—Drs. Hingson, Antes and Cleland used a jet injector—here called a "peace gun" for the first time—to give typhoid inoculations to 486 school children in a half hour. The doctors recognized a new hazard: several of the little boys came through the line a second time in the odd game of "painless shots." Later Dr. Hingson demonstrated use of continuous extradural anesthesia for an abdominal operation, and the patient, feeling no pain while the surgery was in progress, had a cup of tea at exactly 4 P.M., indicating the profundity of the British influence. The team were impressed by the advanced standard of physiotherapy in a Methodist leprosarium in Moulmein.

*Calcutta, India*—Crowded conditions, both in the streets and at the hospitals, resembled those found in Hong Kong and Pusan. Patients were bedded even on the floor under beds in the hospital. "This hospital takes everybody brought to its doors," said the Reverend E. G. T. Madge. "It is better that a sick person re-

ceive treatment on the floor than that he be turned
away." The team saw with their own eyes starvation
and mass burial of the refugees in the Shealda Rail-
way Station in Calcutta—called by Nehru "the dere-
lict city."

*New Delhi, India*—Indian health authorities reported that overpopulation is the land's biggest health
problem. "Epidemics have taken a big drop in ten
years," said Dr. S. C. Seal. "But when you take sickness of one kind out of our country, you produce more
of another, because population is our problem, and
space and food can't keep pace with reproduction."

*Teheran, Iran*—A nation-wide shortage of doctors
was evident, and the Minister of Health pleaded with
American educators to encourage Iranian students
trained for medicine in America to return to Iran. Iran
has practically conquered malaria and now is center-
ing its health efforts in a fight against tuberculosis and
leprosy.

*Cairo, Egypt*—The mission team found its warmest
welcome here. Government red tape was cut to permit
part of the team to travel to Gaza to view the work of
Dr. James M. Young and the mission hospital on the
Gaza Strip. Here they immunized against polio every
child under four in Gaza. Members of the team participated in surgery and other medical care in both Cairo
and Gaza. Dr. Hingson's use of a portable anesthesia
machine to relieve pain of a youthful accident victim
won many new friends. Their host in Egypt: Dr. Nor
El Din Toroff, President Nasser's third-ranking cabinet
member.

*Nairobi, Kenya*—After an automobile trip into the
jungle, conducted by missionary Earl R. Martin on
Saturday, the team attended Sunday worship services
in a grass-thatched mud church at Riruta, a native village in Mau Mau territory. Dr. Black addressed the

congregation through a Kikuya interpreter. The people's respect for cattle as a medium of exchange—two cows were enough to buy a wife!—resulted in a lack of meat to eat and a protein deficiency for the population.

*Mbeya, Tanganyika*—Some of the mission team members enjoyed a safari and brought back to Mbeya about 4,000 pounds of meat, which they gave to villagers. It was estimated the food would last eight villages some three or four days, a contribution to the people's protein deficiency. Tuberculosis is another health problem here. Medical facilities are inadequate, and two general practitioners serve the 30,000 people in Mbeya and some 100,000 to 150,000 in the surrounding area.

*Sanyati, Southern Rhodesia*—A Baptist mission has placed a small hospital, schools and missionary houses amid an area of sand, palms and termite hills. It seeks to bring Christianity, health and education to the people. Dr. Giles Fort, his wife and other missionaries hope to correct tribal customs and superstition not consistent with good health practices.

*Vanga Sur Kwilu Par Kikwit, Belgian Congo*—Drs. Black, Dibble and Payne made complete rounds of the Vanga hospital's hundred patients and uncounted hundreds in out-patient clinics. Dr. Black performed seven difficult operations which the hospital had been "saving" for his visit. Maximum cost of an operation in Vanga is $7. Childbirth delivery is $2, and this includes the gift of a blanket. Dr. Payne conducted a clinic for babies. Sanitary water and better education were seen as major needs of the area.

*Lambaréné, French Equatorial Africa*—The team's visit to Dr. Albert Schweitzer's famed hospital had an odd twist: Mrs. Robertson became ill and was treated by Dr. Schweitzer. The visiting doctors, welcomed to a full inspection of the health facilities, observed: "The great frustration of the work here is that so many improved or cured patients are discharged only to return to the same infectious jungle communities and unhygienic ways of life that caused their original sickness. Ignorance is really the greatest enemy to health." After hearing of the team's round-the-world trip, Dr. Schweitzer, smiling, observed: "I think you have traveled as much as John Foster Dulles."

*Ire, Nigeria*—The King of Ire asked the missionaries for a men's hospital to supplement a mission medical center which has beds for women and children only. Doctors performed several operations at the hospital at Ogbomosho. They visited also the new, modern British hospital at Ibadan.

*Monrovia, Liberia*—Dr. Dibble and Dr. Hingson visited the work of the national Baptist convention and attended the World Health Organization's regional conference on Africa. More than 50 per cent of the population has malaria or bilharzia (snail disease). The doctors also viewed a smallpox pesthouse in which ninety-four critically ill cases are packed on uncovered dirty army cots. Nurses working twelve-hour shifts are themselves sick from exhaustion. For them Dr. Dibble shed tears of sympathy as he prayed audibly under the nearest palm tree, "Oh, God, I have seen more suffering here than at the Crucifixion. Help us to find the way to bring help."

When the huge plane brought the team back to a runway at New York's International Airport, Dr. Hingson summarized the past hundred days for waiting reporters.

The team had traveled 45,000 miles in a huge figure-eight circle across Asia, Europe and Africa. They used many means of transportation—plane, ship, train, jeep, landrover, bus, donkey and camel, and their own good shoe leather—"covering every significant mile," in Dr. Hingson's words, "in the belief that God was using us for a purpose."

Vital statistics included these items:

• Members of the team surveyed exactly 100 hospitals of both missionary and national sponsorship.

• Performed, either as consultants or primary surgeons, 120 operations.

• Administered and delivered more than 90,000 vaccinations for poliomyelitis, typhoid fever and tetanus—proving the efficiency of the jet gun for the first time on a mass scale.

• Distributed more than $100,000 worth of medical supplies and drugs and books, a total transported weight of more than three tons.

• Immunized every child in Gaza under four against polio and provided 5,000 doses of polio Salk vaccine for children of the Vatican Secretariat as a surprise gift to Pope Pius XII.

• Delivered 128 medical lectures to audiences of more than 5,500 in missionary and national university centers.

• Conducted or gave devotionals, sermons or religious lectures to 96 audiences in 27 countries, with a total attendance of 12,000.

• Participated in 47 conferences with national government and health leaders. President William V. S. Tubman of Liberia and some others viewed their health offering as a major avenue of missionary and government partnership.

"Much of the trip was inspiring as we viewed closely the historic progress of man. Much of it was saddening as we experienced the results of ignorance, poverty, disease and man's inhumanity to man," Dr. Hingson said.

He praised the more than 200 missionaries who, alerted by the Baptist World Alliance, had served as their hosts "in opening the inner portals of two continents." And then he added: "They are the unsung heroes and heroines of our age, who have actually opened up the avenues of man to his brother through courage, faith and dedication."

"What did you learn?" the reporters wanted to know.

It was a question the doctor had anticipated. "I can tell you the world's fundamental health needs in ten words—all beginning with the letter S," he said. And then he listed the needs: (1) Sanitation, (2) Sewers, (3) Sprays, (4) Screens, (5) Schools, (6) Soup, (7) Shots, (8) Shoes, (9) Self-respect, and (10) Salvation.

The primary needs, he said in agreement with all other members of the team, are in the fields of public health and nutrition.

"These needs must be supplied before the medical specialties of surgery, radiology, anesthesia, pathology and physical therapy can be intelligently and effectively developed in these countries."

He emphasized that it was a matter of great urgency.

"Never before has the scientific welfare of six continents presented itself before the medical profession with such a limited time table. We, the physicians, can and must extinguish the flames of mass disease and suffering in the vanguard of civilization's most promising era."

The members of the traveling team were convinced. The job that lay ahead was one of mapping a program and enlisting support.

# VI. Brother's Brother Is Born

Members of the survey trip returned to their homes in early October, trying to catch up on their own business affairs and gain a needed rest. All the while, each of them meditated on the things they had seen—for though the picture of a world in trouble could be photographed on the brain during the period of their trip, much more time was needed for the mind to digest the many elements of this picture and put it all in perspective.

Their concern for the world's needs and their enthusiasm for finding medical help had only intensified in the two-month period before Mr. Denny called them back to Washington.

He asked them to come on a weekend, Saturday, November 22, and be prepared to stay through Thanksgiving week. He told them he wanted them to report as individuals on their impressions of the world's needs and their thoughts on what can and should be done to match man's resources to meet these needs.

Several of the men spoke in Washington pulpits on Sunday morning. They met that afternoon in the Denny home, in suburban Virginia, away from the ringing of office telephones and the noise of city traffic.

The location was appropriate in another way also, for the Denny family itself had contributed much to the success of the survey trip. Mary Gunn Denny, the mother of three children, had voluntarily served as secretary in the survey's planning stages. She helped plan the trip's itinerary. She applied her knowledge of world missions to the job of arranging contact personnel for the team at each of its stops in thirty-two countries. She composed and typed hundreds of letters which set the logistics in motion. It was no small job to arrange the mechanics of a project which had no precedent!

Their first half hour together in the Denny home was given to happy memories. They could now smile at their frustrations over missed airplane connections in Africa. And they laughed heartily as Maybelle and Gabe Payne retold the story of their eagerness to get to a hotel room with its promised private bath in Madras; and then they found that the "bath" consisted of a drain hole in the floor and a barrel of rain water with a bucket for a dipper!

Soon, however, the doctors grasped the problems they had come to discuss: how to match the world's resources with the needs they had found.

They first voted to organize a permanent action committee to continue the work that was started. They chose Dr. Hingson as chairman and Dr. Antes as vice chairman. They asked Mr. Denny for permission to use his office at the Baptist World Alliance as a clearinghouse for information and future planning.

What about a name for their new committee? Mrs. Josephine Robertson, the journalist for the expedition, had found it necessary to have a designation for the group in her daily newspaper, the Cleveland *Plain Dealer*, which documented the team's travels and daily service. She called them and their trip: "Project:

Brother's Keeper." It was a phrase with a Biblical context (Genesis 4:9), and it spoke to the man on the street of godly people in an affluent America reaching out in compassion to less fortunate people in other lands. The team, during its Asian and African travels, had more or less adopted Mrs. Robertson's designation.

Dr. Arnold T. Ohrn, general secretary of the Baptist World Alliance, who knew several languages in addition to his native Norwegian, pointed out that "Brother's Keeper" had a note of condescension intertwined with the idea of compassion. He said that if we all are citizens of one world, working on a mission of love, certainly no part of the name should imply that the team looked condescendingly on any other human being.

Dr. Hingson then recalled his brief verbal exchange with a Nigerian medical student, Victor Lawoyin. (It was a conversation that had meant no more than a brief delay and perhaps even minor irritation as the doctors had worked so rapidly in the African heat, but now it had relevance in the light of Christian love.)

Lawoyin had objected to the term "Brother's Keeper" in Lagos newspaper headlines. "We do not need a keeper," he said emphatically. "We need a brother. What you have shown us is better described by the words, 'Brother's Brother.'"

And thus on a Sunday afternoon, the concept that had grown in the minds of these people for years gained both an organizational format and a name. They brought into being the "Brother's Brother Foundation." The American professors and specialists humbly became students before the wisdom of an African.

Then the group tried to set down on paper the program needed to reach their lofty objective of contributing to world health, of extending a helping hand rather than a handout.

(Later, the Nigerian who named the Foundation was supported by the team throughout his medical education in Albany, N.Y. Now, after three years' residency, Dr. Lawoyin has returned with his wife, who is from Sierra Leone, to Nigeria as a physician to his people.)

Mr. Denny, the team's home base coordinator and the beloved friend of each team member, jotted on his note pad each suggestion as the group's members responded. They finished the afternoon and evening session with several lists.

First of all they reduced to paper, as best they could, the outstanding needs they saw in the missions they visited:

1. Practically every country needed to develop public health tools, to educate the people in the principles of good health, and to apply health principles in both public and private areas. It was suggested that missionaries from all churches be given orientation courses in public health, so that they might augment the present meager medical personnel in extending health education throughout the world.

2. The level of nutrition must be improved, since at least one third of the world was on substandard food allotments and without proper nutrition planning. This emphasis was a major dividend of the understanding of the two dieticians, Mrs. Hingson and Mrs. Antes.

3. Food production must be increased to provide proper food materials. Mr. Hudson Titmus, a Petersburg, Virginia, layman who had joined the conference at Mr. Denny's invitation, told of his hope that the state's agricultural colleges would use his new 800-acre farm in Virginia to train nationals from overseas

in modern agricultural principles so that they could raise the standards of living in their home countries.

4. Good dental care must be made available to the people of Asia and Africa. Nigeria, for instance, had only sixteen dentists for its 1958 population of 34 million. It was suggested that assistant dentists and technicians be trained in the various countries for service to their own people.

The men and women present knew that much of the burden for meeting these needs rested in their own enthusiastic outreach, on the influence of their reports. They, fifteen of them, were the ones who had been privileged to see these needs; now they were responsible for using their rare knowledge to call the world's affluent people to the side of the world's needy.

They agreed among themselves to speak to civic clubs, to churches, to medical societies and to universities at every opportunity; to use their pens to write the story in monographs for their medical journals, in newspaper reports, and perhaps in a book; to make the twenty-one hours of motion-picture film they had exposed during their trip available to any church-related studio that could edit it and gain wide audiences; and to compile, in future meetings and through correspondence, plans for development of health facilities they visited.

On Monday night of Thanksgiving week, U. S. Government health and foreign aid officials joined executive leaders of Christian mission societies at the Baptist Building in Washington to hear the traveling doctors tell their story. It was a unique audience even for cosmopolitan Washington. And it was a long meeting—from six to half past eleven—as the doctors each told their story with the use of slides and film clips and then patiently answered the questions of people who wanted to know still more.

The meeting was as spiritually inspiring as it was medically enlightening.

Dr. Antes spoke with the experience of a veteran physician whose long-existing concern for world need had been infinitely intensified.

"Those of you who are familiar with the Scripture will remember the story of the return of the seventy and how they came rejoicing at what things they saw. And Christ and his disciples were watching as they gave their report—much as you people are watching us tonight—and Christ turned to his disciples and said, 'The things that you see and you hear, prophets and kings have longed to see and to hear and have not heard.'

"That's in the experience of this team. We have seen and heard things that very few people have had the marvelous opportunity to see and hear. I assure you it's the feeling of every member of this team that the rest of our lives we will try to see that our efforts will be put to good use in the Master's cause."

Then he continued:

"If there's anything we've learned on this trip, it is that *just* education is not enough, it must be *Christian* education. Just to educate a person doesn't necessarily make him a brother's keeper, but to see the devotion, the consecration, of the missionaries who preceded us to some of these areas by as much as a hundred and fifty years is indeed a great thrill.

"Wherever we saw hospitals and schools where missionaries have assumed that people have the potentiality of a human being and have worked from that point of view to educate them and convert them and Christianize them, we see this marvelous development. But wherever they tried to exploit them or where they considered that they were all morons, you didn't see progress. And that's one of the great things we learned—

the effect of Christian evangelism wherever it is practiced.

"We have seen these people who are just a few years out of jungle huts now giving anesthesia in the operating room or acting as assistants to surgeons and, in some places, we have seen them with Ph.D. degrees from Columbia at the head of school systems and as doctors in the teaching systems. It has been a truly remarkable experience."

Dr. Payne, the pediatrician, told of his surprise when he found no harelips among the children of African villages. A missionary answered that he too had asked the same question several years before—only to discover that all babies born into non-Christian families with any sort of deformity were "disposed of immediately in the most convenient manner of the jungle." Missionary education is helping to overcome such superstitions and taboos, he said, and missionary hospitals are healing the deformities surgically.

Dr. Black, the surgeon, told of meeting a man with a small knot on his leg and a tremendous tumor on his neck. He asked that the insignificant knot be removed, but refused the doctor's pleas that he might surgically remove the neck tumor also. But on Sunday the man came to the mission house and told Dr. Black he had changed his mind. The tumor was successfully removed, and then the man confessed he had feared earlier that if he submitted to the neck surgery somebody would cast a spell on him and he would die.

The crowd chuckled when he told of a Congolese youth who was serving as an orderly, taking more and more responsibility in the operating room. "I asked this young man to chart a time schedule for operations the following day, and I said, 'We'll start at seven thirty in the morning.' And he said, 'Does the doctor want to start scrubbing at seven thirty, or does he want to start cutting?' "

Perhaps the most inspiring speaker of the evening was Dr. Dibble, the always-smiling, deep-thinking Negro doctor from Tuskegee. He looked hopefully to the future by pointing out that "all the problems we have been showing you tonight have been eradicated in America many years ago."

"The number one problem in all these foreign countries, whether it's in India or in Africa, is public health," he said.

"We eradicated smallpox in the South many years ago. We've got tuberculosis pretty well eradicated. We've got malaria and the intestinal diseases under control. And certainly we are making advances in heart disease, and we have cleared up syphilis. These are the problems in Asia and Africa. What they still need is the good American know-how.

"Certainly I think it is the consensus of all the men who were on this trip that in addition to supporting missions that we have lagged in the support of the American government in what they are trying to do in the field of health and education to help foreign countries. When I go to pay what little income tax I have to pay, I certainly will pay it with a larger smile than I have done before."

Dr. Dibble continued:

"I remember way back in the 1914's and 15's when in the South we had plenty of hookworms. We don't see hookworms any more. We put shoes on. We could keep American factories busy just developing shoes to eradicate hookworms. It would cost money, yes. But isn't it better to spend it that way than to spend it in guns and airplanes to kill somebody?

"The work of the missionaries is not over. It's just

beginning. The world is built on change. But the only thing that is going to change the moral fiber of the world is the Christian religion. And if there was ever a time that we need to put money and not only money, but our whole fiber, our whole souls, all of our funds into the improvement of the world's people, now is the time. We have a great challenge, a great opportunity, and certainly I believe that the American people and the people throughout the world are going to be able to take that leadership through the Christian religion in order that we may eradicate these problems. It's going to take work, it's going to take a lot of time."

Dr. Hingson was the last speaker of the long evening. He told the medical and church leaders that the world's health needs are so vast that they cannot be met by any one church group or any single government. He pleaded for cooperation between government and religiously oriented medical men in providing materials and personal service.

He confessed that even after their weeks of consideration in their homes and offices and their days together in Washington, the doctors were unable to outline a program that would miraculously and overnight solve the problem. He did, however, make several proposals for actions that would move toward the goal.

He proposed that all religious groups enlarge and strengthen their medical missions programs. "The constant meeting of human need—emotional, physical, spiritual—was the keynote of Christ's ministry and is compatible with the central theme of all religions," Dr. Hingson said.

Existing mission clinics and hospitals are a good starting point, he said, because they are already there. Additional personnel should be recruited, both for permanent commitment and for temporary interim service, to assure these hospitals of adequate and well-trained staffs. Doctors should be encouraged to plan their vacations to offer their services to mission hospitals and to lecture to both mission doctors and national medical leaders on the newest medical discoveries. "We propose a volunteer pool of physicians as a basis, to relieve regular mission medical personnel in their furlough years."

He said further that intelligent surveys of world health needs should be made as often as once a year and these findings released to religious, government and independent benevolent groups who have resources to meet these needs. He joined Dr. Cleland in recommending, in addition to personnel, medicine and equipment, the inclusion of medical library books, medical films, and other teaching aids. He urged that doctors who have retired and widows of doctors should be encouraged to donate their instruments and other equipment to meet hospital needs in developing countries.

Special provisions should be made also, Dr. Hingson said, to encourage medical students in developing countries to secure the best possible education either in their own lands or in the educational centers of America and Europe.

Other of his suggestions looked to extension and upbuilding of public health programs throughout the world. These programs would not only include medical care but would give strong emphasis to sanitation and to education of the people in hygiene and health care.

Dr. Hingson expressed hope also that American doctors might be motivated to contribute 1 per cent of their income to a service organization for world health and world peace. "This small contribution would not work a hardship on any doctor," Dr. Hingson said,

"and it would give him an opportunity to work actively toward alleviation of world suffering and toward
world peace."

# VII. Years of Persuasion

The next three years, 1959–62, were years of persuasion. Dr. Hingson, his fifteen traveling colleagues, and a good handful of the people with whom he had talked either individually or in groups served as evangelists for the Brother's Brother obsession.

There were of course doubters. Many people who heard Bob Hingson were captured by his enthusiasm, his energy, his ambitious dreams. Others labeled him an idealist, a dreamer who paid all too little attention to reality. His fast speech, his ambitious programs had all the earmarks, they said, of a "snow job."

But none of the sixteen travelers could be discouraged. They had seen the need. They were convinced that help must be given. They knew that help must come from affluent nations. And all of them, Catholic, Protestants and Jews, recognized that this humanitarian service was in keeping with the best teachings of their churches and synagogues.

In June 1959, the first anniversary of the team's departure date for the 1958 survey, Dr. Hingson wrote a progress report addressed to his "teammates and our missionary colleagues overseas."

He reported that as of June 1, members of the team had addressed audiences of more than 180,000 persons. He himself had spoken 108 times. Dr. Gabe Payne had multiplied his outreach by organizing eighty lay speakers to address churches through his state of Kentucky on the subject of "Operation: Human Need."

"In none of our addresses have we asked for contributions," Dr. Hingson said, observing that "we would rather stimulate giving through established and regular channels." Yet, he said, many gifts had come. One ton of clothing had already been shipped from Oregon City Rotary Clubs to Korea as the result of Dr. Cleland's reports to meetings in his home city.

Team members were meanwhile donating all the honoraria they received to the production costs of motion pictures on the 1958 survey and toward the tuition of the Nigerian medical student, Victor Lawoyin —now a physician in Nigeria. A total of twenty-one hours of film had been shot on the trip, and the raw footage was given to specialists of the Foreign Mission Board and the Radio and Television Commission of the Southern Baptist Convention for editing in thirty-minute segments. Two valuable films were produced, one by each of the organizations—the skilled personnel contributing their time and the Brother's Brother movement paying actual production cost. Paul Harvey, the commentator, had been so impressed by one of Dr. Hingson's speeches that he volunteered his service as commentator on the film edited by the Radio and Television Commission. Bud Collyer was master of ceremonies for another film on nation-wide television.

These films, made available in 1960, were used in churches, schools and at church encampments to call attention to need and to plead for volunteers.

Dr. Cleland, meanwhile, energetically achieved

American Medical Association support for objectives
the Brother's Brother team outlined in their November
1958 meetings. His efforts were channeled through the
Oregon Medical Association, which then appealed to
the annual meetings of A.M.A.'s House of Delegates.

The A.M.A. took significant actions in 1959 and
1960. A clinical session of the A.M.A. House of Delegates, meeting at Dallas in December 1959, received a
resolution from the Oregon society to provide postgraduate education for American physicians in foreign
mission fields.

The resolution recognized that American doctors
working in these overseas posts usually are away from
the States for five-year intervals and there is little opportunity for postgraduate study during this interval.
These doctors are therefore denied access to the new
discoveries and consultation privileges that would normally help them to keep abreast of advances in medicine.

"Be it resolved, therefore," the adopted resolution
stated, "that the House of Delegates of the American
Medical Association does hereby recognize the responsibility of the Association for the postgraduate education of American physicians in the foreign mission
field; and does hereby direct that an appropriate committee of the Association study and make recommendations regarding ways and means of bringing such
educational facilities within the reach of these physicians."

Acting on these instructions, the A.M.A. Board of
Trustees called a meeting in early 1960 of representatives of medical mission groups from both Protestant
and Roman Catholic persuasions and developed plans
for disseminating information in countries where medical missionaries work and for sending qualified physi-

cians to the areas on teaching missions. They also developed plans for good postgraduate training while missionary doctors are in the United States on furlough.

In 1960, the A.M.A. House of Delegates adopted a second Oregon resolution entitled "Emergency Medical Services to Foreign Mission Fields." It recognized that mission hospitals, "established in every uncommitted country of the world," provide a good base in which American medicine can work, even in the presence of political unrest.

"Be it resolved, therefore," their statement said, "that the American Medical Association shall immediately investigate the feasibility of developing a mechanism whereby members of the Association may serve in the foreign mission fields on a temporary basis when emergencies arise and shall then seek volunteer physicians to serve in such capacities."

The resolutions led to development of the A.M.A.'s Department of International Health.

Even prior to this A.M.A. action, the Hingson enthusiasm had provided some of the stimulus for the launching of the Hospital Ship *Hope*. Dr. Hingson had fed copies of his correspondence throughout 1957 and 1958 to his brother, Captain James Monroe Hingson, at the U. S. Navy Submarine Base in New London, Connecticut. Captain Hingson shared the letters with Captain Frank Manson of the Navy, and Captain Manson visualized the use of mothballed Navy ships to touch the world health needs mentioned in Bob Hingson's letters. He talked with Dr. William Walsh of Washington to initiate plans for the now famed hospital ship. He initiated his own plans for Navy medical service in ports around the world in what is now known as the "Great White Fleet."

Dr. Hingson sought to alert all available sources of help to the need, pleading for assignment of resources to meet it. Typical of his letters was one addressed October 4, 1961, to President John F. Kennedy.

Dear Mr. President:

"At least let us begin."

In our world today war still ranks a poor third behind famine and disease in its destructive force on mankind. In 1960 former Surgeon General Thomas Parran stated: "Today the technic of immunization provides protection against all of the significant diseases that have not been eliminated by public health measures or that do not yield readily to chemotherapy."

For the past two decades, as a U. S. Public Health Service officer, and as a university medical school research professor, I have organized and trained a team of 105 physicians and 20 nurses in mass immunization therapy. Significantly also, these physicians are anesthesiologists, well equipped to supervise operating rooms, treat mass casualties, and to conduct the most modern methods in the control of surgical, traumatic and obstetric pain.

At the present time, with equipment now available, we can immunize through jet inoculation technics one patient every four seconds, or 10,000 per day per physician, with electrical power or hand-operated equipment. Already this team has immunized more than one and a half million patients in such programs, as large as 100,000 patients in Cleveland, Ohio; 160,000 in Rhode Island; and 90,000 in a medical mission survey in Asia and Africa.

On seventy-two hours' notice this team, recruited from the faculty of the School of Medicine, Western Reserve University, staff of University Hospitals of Cleveland, and graduate trainees of the program, stands ready to provide two to ten physicians, one technician and one nurse for assistance to medical health authorities in any part of the world where formal request will be made through the World Health Organization; the Pan American Sanitary Bureau; the World Federation of Anesthesiologists; the American Medical Association; or the U.S. Public Health Service, with the understanding that no professional fee compensation will be required beyond full cost of vaccines, medical instruments, round trip travel expenses and full maintenance expense.

In the event a developing country with insufficient budget seeks such services, we would be most active in seeking financial aid through world relief organizations and foundations to provide part or all of the expense involved.

It is my belief that two weeks of service in the field by this team would properly instruct most local medical personnel in this new method of therapy in such a way that they could carry on alone with this new equipment, and subsequently our American team would return to the United States or the country of origin.

In view of the fact that this team is especially skilled in anesthesiology, operating room and recovery room care, it would be pleased to provide teaching service to hospitals and health stations in the area, between inoculation programs.

Significantly also, sixty of these one hundred and five physicians were educated in or have now returned to six countries of the British Commonwealth, Cuba, Germany, Holland, Hungary, India, Iran, Italy, Japan, Latvia, Mexico, the Philippine Islands, Poland, Russia, the Congo and Southern Rhodesia. Members of this team have speaking facility in the following languages: Arabic, Dutch, English, French, German, Italian, Japanese, Russian and Spanish. Forty-five are in the United States, including twenty in our Western Reserve University Department of Anesthesia, and including the six members of our pilot survey: "Operation Brother's Keeper," interracial and inderdenominational medical mission team, with specialty boards in surgery, obstetrics and gynecology, anesthesiology, pediatrics, and internal medicine, and public health.

In this broad field of humanitarian medicine we wish to emphasize that physicians in private practice who have appreciated the opportunities of education and specialization in our great country, are capable of sharing and concerned enough to share our scientific resources with those who need them.

Respectfully,

ROBERT A. HINGSON, M.D.
*Professor of Anesthesia, Western*
*Reserve University*
*Medical and Dental Schools*

*Chairman, Relief Committee of the*
*World Federation of Anesthesiologists*

*Senior Surgeon, U. S. Public Health*
*Service (R)*

Ralph A. Dungan, a presidential assistant, responded, advising that the President "appreciates the willingness of your members to share their knowledge and skills for the relief of misery and death in the world." Mr. Dungan said that he was, at the President's request, passing copies of Dr. Hingson's letter to the U. S. Department of Health, Education and Welfare, to the World Health Organization, and to the medical staffs of the Peace Corps and the International Cooperation Administration—now the Agency for International Development, more usually called AID.

The public was thus being alerted to world needs and to the urgency of American medical and religious people to apply this country's resources to meet those needs.

But still the next—and one of the most significant—developments rested on the initiative of the Brother's Brother team itself. Dr. Hingson and his colleagues were to prove, in 1962, the practical side of their idealism.

# VIII. The Death of Smallpox in Liberia

The Republic of Liberia, about the size of Ohio and with a population of 1,066,000, was a logical choice for Brother's Brother's first major demonstration for the mass immunization, crash program technique.

The survey team had visited there in 1958. Dr. Hingson and Dr. Dibble had observed an outbreak of smallpox that left lifetime blemishes on hundreds and claimed other uncounted scores of dead. They learned that poor nutrition and tropical diseases reduce the average life expectancy to thirty to thirty-five years. Thirty-two per cent of all live-born children died within the first twelve months of life, and another 12.67 per cent were carried to cemeteries in early childhood.

Dr. Hingson knew that health standards were low primarily because of its climate astride the equator. High humidity encourages almost perpetual growth—not only of vegetation but of every parasite, germ, and disease-carrying insect.

"The people are unhealthy because the germs are so healthy," he said. Even the healthy tsetse fly had killed off most of the country's cattle, a prime source of protein.

Despite these health problems, Liberia was a for-

ward-looking nation. Its great rubber plantations and
industries developed by Firestone, Goodyear, Good-
rich, U. S. and Republic Steel and other American
companies have brought a measure of economic stabil-
ity. American ties date back as far as 1820, when the
American Colonization Society first established in Liberia new homes for American Negroes freed from
slavery. A freed slave, the Reverend Lott Carey, had
come to Liberia in 1821, bringing with him a congregation who had organized their own African Baptist
Church in Richmond, Virginia, and moved it to a Liberian site they called Monrovia (now the capital
city) in honor of American President James Monroe.

Dr. Hingson's personal interest in Liberia was in-
creased because he is a descendent of President
Monroe. There were religious ties too. Dr. William V.
S. Tubman,* president of the Republic since 1943, is a
Methodist minister, and Dr. William R. Tolbert, Jr.,
vice president of the Republic, is a Baptist minister.
(Dr. Tolbert was elected president of the Baptist
World Alliance at its 1965 Congress in Miami Beach.)

Dr. Hingson talked with Dr. Tolbert personally
about the purposes of his new foundation and outlined
plans whereby he could bring a staff of doctors and
technicians into Liberia to work with Liberian medical
authorities in combating the spread of pestilential diseases.

The thoroughness of his planning is illustrated in a
subsequent letter to Dr. Tubman. Dr. Hingson said:

In public addresses by radio and television, before
audiences of churches, schools, universities, service clubs
and government groups, the six doctors of the Baptist

* President Tubman's grandmother was born adjacent to Dr.
Hingson's father's farm in Alabama as a slave girl of a neighbor.

World Alliance Medical Mission Survey Team have
reached approximately 9 million Americans with the
message of the people in the developing countries in Asia
and Africa. There is quite a ground swell of compassion
on the part of the medical profession in our countries and
in many others.

More than a score of physicians from all parts of the
United States have volunteered to give four months to
one year of their time in rendering a service to the people
of Africa, Asia, and South America.

During the past two years we have had four conferences with Ambassador George Padmore and one conference with Dr. Murray Barclay, the Liberian surgeon
general, concerning development of the plan. Indeed, following the visit of Dr. Roakford L. Weeks, president of
the University of Liberia, to Cleveland, President John
Schoff Millis of Western Reserve University and I ex-
plored with executives of the Firestone Plantations Company and the Republic Steel Corporation mechanisms
whereby American medical education might participate
with industry in cooperating with the Republic of Liberia
in providing some essential health services.

All of us feel that in order to render the most effective
service a long-term plan must be developed based on an
intense two-month survey to be conducted by the Western Reserve University College of Medicine. The Firestone Plantations Company is developing the first step of
the project by extending invitations to the Medical College to assign two of its senior faculty for purposes of
this survey. This team will work closely with the designated representatives of the Surgeon General of Liberia.

The letter went on to explain that results of the survey would be studied by interested parties in the United States and that a team of physicians and medical
student technicians "will be selected for mass immunization projects throughout the villages and cities of
the entire nation of Liberia." He said also that he had

talked in person with Vice President Richard Nixon of the United States and with the chief of U. S. Naval operations Admiral Arleigh Burke, concerning the possibility of using a Navy ship to transport the team of supplies from America to a Liberian port, and the use of helicopters to take members of the team to inland centers for vaccination clinics.

He explained that the Pharmaceutical Manufacturers Association might consider provision of smallpox and poliomyelitis vaccines if the survey team designated these as priority projects in Liberia. He proposed further that other medicines be given for typhoid, cholera, diphtheria, yellow fever, yaws, venereal disease, and intestinal parasites.

"All of the organizations mentioned above would like to participate as a partner with the people and the government of Liberia in this type of humanitarian undertaking," Dr. Hingson's proposal concluded. "Our ultimate aim would be the improvement of the health of Liberia through preventive medicine, and the application of active treatment where indicated for existing diseases."

Dr. Tubman responded favorably by cablegram to the proposal. Dr. Hingson launched arrangements through a barrage of letters, telegrams and telephone calls to manufacturers and possible contributors throughout America.

Dr. Hingson and Dr. Thomas Parran flew to Liberia in early January 1962 for a survey of opportunities and an outlining of plans. Dr. Parran was a former Surgeon General of the United States and was a key figure in the development of the World Health Organization. He was Dr. Hingson's superior officer for thirteen years.

A team of twenty-one workers was recruited. There

were nine medical doctors: Robert Hingson, Thomas
Parran, Jack Cole,* Theodore Parran, Blanchard
Antes, Ralph Rusynyk, Ernest Hopkins,† Lewis
Abram, and Anthony J. Tomaro. There were four medical students: Dick Carruthers, Arthur Bankhurst,
Dick Auburn, and Dick Hingson, Dr. Hingson's oldest
son. Two dieticians, two school teachers, a postal em-
ployee, a minister, Dr. Francis Wheaton of Dr. Hingson's church, and two sons of doctors completed the
list of volunteer personnel.

The team was interracial, with two Negroes linking
hands with nineteen whites. It was interfaith, with
volunteers coming from Roman Catholic, Greek Orthodox, Jewish, and Protestant groups. The Protestants
included members of the Baptist, Methodist, Lutheran, Presbyterian and Episcopal churches.

Companies affiliated with the Pharmaceutical Manufacturers Association contributed thousands of dollars worth of vaccines, medicines and other supplies.
Dr. Hingson mortgaged his home for $25,000 to meet
still uncovered costs. Congresswoman Frances P. Bol-
ton, long a knowledgeable friend and explorer of Africa, rendered major diplomatic and consultative assistance for both the 1958 and this 1962 operational plan.
Congressman Brooks Hays as Assistant Secretary of
State provided diplomatic clearance for use of the
peace guns.

The United States Navy (with support of the chief
of U. S. Naval operations Admiral Arleigh Burke) provided transportation on a 15,000-ton ammunition ship,
the U.S.S. Diamond Head, commanded by Captain
James Monroe Hingson, Bob Hingson's brother. Pas-

---

* Now professor of Surgery at Yale University in New Haven.
† Associate professor of Obstetrics and Gynecology at Howard
University.

sengers and cargo assembled at Newport News, Virginia, and the ship set sail February 2, 1962.

Their twelve-day ocean crossing was not without tragedy. Pharmacist Carl Frode, a representative of Eli Lilly & Company, had spent the full day of February 5, with other members of the team, sorting heavy boxes of pharmaceutical materials to make an inventory of all that was aboard. The strain was too much for him. He collapsed, and despite the efforts of the doctors aboard he died of a heart attack.

The inventory also turned up an alarming fact. The pharmaceutical houses had promised 1 million doses of smallpox vaccine. Only 10,000 doses could be found. It was obvious that somehow in the rush of shipping, a disastrous error had been made. But the ship was four days at sea, and there was no turning back. A radiogram for additional material was sent out but Dr. Hingson realized that weeks more would be required for its delivery to Liberia.

This seemingly tragic shortage became the setting for a story that Dr. Hingson calls the miracle of five loaves and two fishes. He went to bed that night with the unhappy discovery haunting his every thought. But his mind also flashed to memory of the Bible story where Jesus fed a multitude of five thousand people with a simple lunch brought by a single boy in the audience.

During his fitful sleep that night on the rolling waves of a disturbed ocean, the doctor realized that the application of medicines with a jet injector had one highly significant difference from the conventional multiple-puncture vaccination technique. Doctors using the conventional method place a "dose" of the vaccine on the patient's upper arm and then use a needle to make many punctures into the skin so that the vaccine can make its way below the skin's surface.

But the jet gun sprays every dose in several hundreds of particles, and, Dr. Hingson reasoned, even one tiny particle of the live virus vaccine should be sufficient to alert the blood's antibodies to set up resistance to it. This is the way that immunization is attained.

Dr. Hingson rationalized that vaccine propelled through a jet gun could be diluted. All of a jet shot goes into the flesh and spreads in the optimum dermal layer because of the high pressure behind it, whereas the traditional multiple-puncture technique is dependent on only a fraction of the dose being absorbed.

Dr. Hingson explained his theory to his brother, Captain Hingson, and to other doctors aboard. Members of the team and 300 members of the crew volunteered their arms for tests of the various dilutions of vaccine. Jet guns were unpacked, and Dr. Hingson diluted the vaccine in three different ways. Some got a dilution of 1 to 10, some 1 to 25, and others 1 to 50. Three days later he checked their arms, and discovered that every man had a positive take! One dentist who had never had a positive in four previous vaccinations got a swelling—blister—pustule—scab—scar with the vaccine diluted 1 to 25.

Medical history was being made. Once the ship docked on the Liberian shore, Dr. Hingson explained to Vice President Tolbert his dilemma of too little vaccine and the successful test of his dilution theory on board the *U.S.S. Diamond Head*. Could he experiment further, he asked, on Liberian soldiers?

"I believe the Bible, and I believe that Christ can use the little offerings we have available to accomplish great good," Dr. Tolbert said. "You have permission to experiment with the whole Liberian army."

The tests again proved the validity of Dr. Hingson's theory. But rather than stretch the doses too far, team members agreed on a dilution of 1 to 11. The 10,000

available doses were stretched to give smallpox vaccinations to 110,000 people! Other vaccine arrived from
New York by the time this initial supply was exhausted. Since the dilution of 1 to 11 had proved its worth,
the new vaccine was similarly multiplied.

Even as they prepared to launch their efforts, team
members learned of 400 new cases of smallpox. People
were dying every day. A sort of hysteria swept the
country. In one village a little boy with smallpox was
stoned to drive him into the bush. Dr. Hingson heard
of the episode and followed a repentant villager into
the jungle to rescue the child. Dr. Hingson carried the
crying, injured and grateful little boy 2 miles on his
back to a pesthouse hospital in the night.

Yet their fear of smallpox, dreadful though it was,
was not enough to draw Liberians to the visiting doctors. They had another fear—fear of the needle. Previous attempts to immunize with the needle had resulted in almost total failure. Many who submitted
their arms for vaccination used lime juice to neutralize
the effect of the medication. And their rubbing of the
multiple-punctured area resulted in infection and
scarification—without immunization. Many people
thus infected died from tetanus. Two such victims had
just died at the Lutheran Hospital at Zorzor.

But the use of the jet gun without a needle won its
converts one by one. Those who were convinced of the
painlessness of the new method told their friends, and
this word of mouth was reinforced by stories in the
newspapers and announcements on the radio. Every
person who was vaccinated carried his own advertis-
ing—a Band-Aid,* which in itself became to the Liberians a badge of honor. Suddenly there came an as-
tonishing response. Children who had once hidden

* One million Band-Aids were donated by Johnson & Johnson.

from the doctors rushed forward with outstretched
arms, crying, "Here, me."

The bandages in fact proved to be a major psycho-
logical factor in the crusade. On one occasion when
the supply of patches became temporarily exhausted,
the patients gladly took a card certifying their vaccination and walked several miles to another source of
supply. Witch doctors who first opposed them joined
the teams when given the position of "Band-Aider."

For two months the volunteer doctors worked from
city to city, village to village, carrying their peace
guns and preventive medicine. They went by helicopter to scattered airfields, where tribesmen had
gathered on the airstrips in response to pleas by the
health service and the Liberian army. They set up
roadblocks, and asked riders in cars, wagons and buses
to stick out their arms for vaccination. They went to
sporting events and every other spot where a crowd
was expected to gather. When their electric-powered
jet gun interfered with the public-address system at a
championship soccer game between Liberia and Guin-
ea for the then prized Nkrumah Cup, they shut off the
power and used hand guns until every one of the five
thousand spectators was immunized.

Dr. Hingson estimated that an average of 80 per
cent of the people were immunized. But he attempted
to make the job complete with a hut-to-hut canvas. In-
stead of running away, those who had not voluntarily
come to the earlier clinics now presented their arms
for injection—indicating they were good losers in a
game similar to cops and robbers.

In addition to smallpox vaccine, the team gave protection for yellow fever. The pharmaceutical industry
sent 1 million doses of penicillin to treat yaws, a disease of the skin and bone caused by spirochetes—but

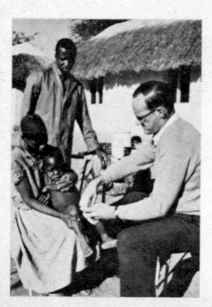

Ralph Hingson, son of the doctor, gave his shirt to Jesus, a Honduran boy crippled with tuberculosis of the bone. Ralph took the boy's shirt back to Cleveland as a reminder of world poverty.

Hundreds of doctors have been inspired by Operation Brother's Brother to volunteer their services to medical centers overseas. Here, Dr. Ernest J. Gregory of San Antonio, Texas, bandages a burned knee in Rhodesia. *(Southern Baptist Foreign Mission Board photo.)*

These are the doctors who made up the Baptist World Alliance Medical Mission Survey in 1958, giving Brother's Brother its start. They are Dr. Gabe Payne, Dr. Eugene H. Dibble, Dr. Charles L. Black, Dr. Robert A. Hingson, Dr. John G. P. Cleland, and Dr. Blanchard Antes.

Dr. Robert A. Hingson, left, joins Dr. Ramon Chikiamco and Dr. Felino Barnes in examining a patient at the Children's Memorial Hospital at Manila, The Philippines. Both physicians are former students of Dr. Hingson.

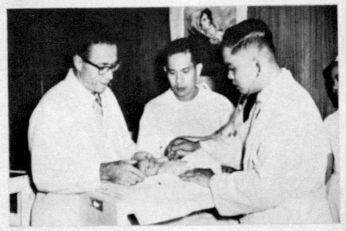

The 1958 survey team stopped at Lambaréné, French Equatorial Africa, now Republic of Gabon, to visit with Dr. Albert Schweitzer at his jungle hospital. Shown here are Dr. Antes, Dr. Hingson, Dr. Schweitzer, Dr. Cleland, Dr. Black, and Dr. Payne.

Dr. Hingson and his brother, Capt. James Monroe Hingson, stand below a portrait of their ancestor, President James Monroe, hanging in the capitol at Monrovia, Liberia. Capt. Hingson was commander of the U.S.S. Diamond Head, which transported the Brother's Brother team and supplies to Liberia in 1962.

*(Photo by Clarence Duncan.)*

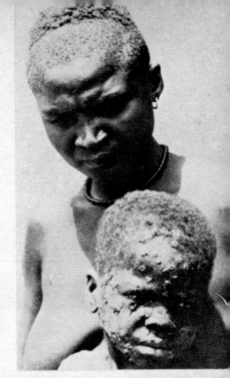

Yaws is a widespread disfiguring disease afflicting an estimated 50 million people. It can be cured by a single injection of penicillin. These pictures *(Eric Schwab, World Health Organization)* show a Nigerian child before and after treatment.

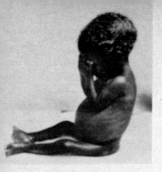

Hunger is a disease of millions, and its effects are seen here in this child's bloated belly and matchstick legs. Malnutrition caused by protein deficiency is called Kwashiorkor. *(Photo by Food and Agriculture Organization of the United Nations.)*

Smallpox was one of the major killers in Liberia before the Brother's Brother team went to work.

Meningitis afflicts 40,000 young persons, killing 3,000 of them each year, in the "meningitis belt" of central Africa. A single injection of sulfonamides, at the start of the disease, gives a 90 per cent chance of complete recovery. *(Photo by D. Henrioud, World Health Organization.)*

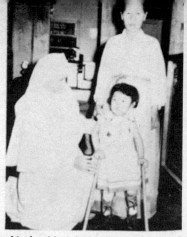

At the Maryknoll Sisters' hospital in Pusan, Korea, Sister Maura Therese fits a 5-year-old polio victim with braces. The child's mother stands behind her.

Miss Mary Degler, right, part of the 1958 survey team, gives a cholera shot to an orphan in India. Mother Theresa, Missionaries of Charity, assists.

Dr. Hingson, left, and Dr. Payne treat a small patient at the Baptist clinic in Hong Kong. He was said to be the 10,000th patient at the clinic operated by Dr. S. G. Rankin.

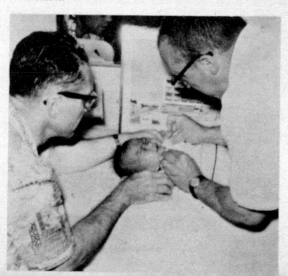

Poster boards, such as this, supplemented newspapers, radios and sound trucks in calling persons to vaccination centers in Nicaragua.

Mrs. Hingson, the doctor's wife, is equally untiring in her repeated "vacation" trips for immunization projects. Here she drops poliomyelitis vaccine on the tongue of a Nicaraguan child.

Members of the Brother's Brother team took their guns to Sunday school at the First Baptist Church at Managua, Nicaragua. Dr. Gustavo Parajon, a native Nicaraguan and a Hingson student, is giving shots at the left.

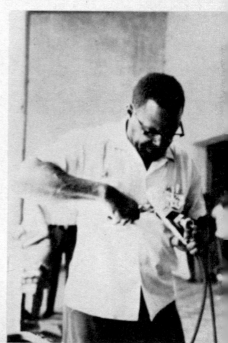

Albert Burroughs, orderly in University Hospitals at Cleveland, has accompanied Dr. Hingson on most of his trips. He overhauls every gun each night to guarantee satisfactory performance the next day.

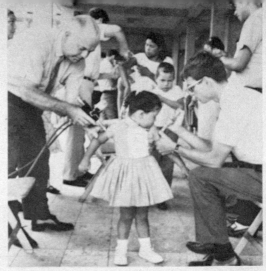

This Nicaraguan miss, like 137,000 of her fellow countrymen, gets two shots at the same time. The father-and-son team above, Dr. Harry C. Helm and his son Clay, simultaneously give smallpox (left arm) and leprosy-tuberculosis (right arm) vaccines.

Cyril E. Bryant, author of this book and maker of most of these photographs, tries his own hand with a jet gun. He says the girl cried before the shot, not afterwards.

Team members fan out each morning from central cities to rural vaccination clinics to go where the people are. Conveyances range from burros to airplanes and are furnished by the host government.

Dr. Hingson answers health questions of many persons who come to his vaccination clinics. Here he examines an aged woman with suspected skin cancer.

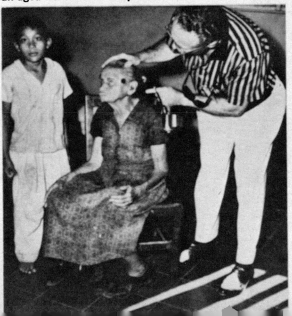

**First person in this vaccination line at Ricks Institute, Monrovia, Liberia, is William R. Tolbert, Jr., vice president of the Republic of Liberia. Dr. Tolbert has since been elected president of the Baptist World Alliance.** *(Liberian photos by Clarence Duncan, Baptist Radio and Television Commission.)*

**Brother's Brother took books and garden seed, along with vaccine, on their trip to Liberia in 1962. They felt that good agriculture and good education would help secure health gains.**

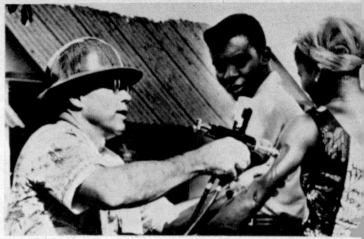

Dr. Hingson uses an electric-powered motor jet for vaccinations in this urban center in Liberia. Hand-pumped guns are used in rural areas where electricity is not available.

Teaching is a major part of the Brother's Brother emphasis. Dr. Hingson is shown here training the Liberian Surgeon General and grandson of a former president, Dr. Edwin Murray Barclay. At the far left is Dr. Pauli Lieberman, the Jewish volunteer member colleague of the Foundation from Haifa, Israel and presently serving in Dr. Hingson's department at University Hospitals.

While Dr. Hingson was demonstrating his technique to Costa Rican health authorities in June 1967, an advance team of Dr. and Mrs. José Amoedo (left) and Robert F. Miller flew to Panama to offer the team's help there. Dr. Alberto Calvo (back to camera) is national health minister of Panama.

These parents and their children wait outside the Costa Rican Ministry of Health at San José for measles vaccine for the children.

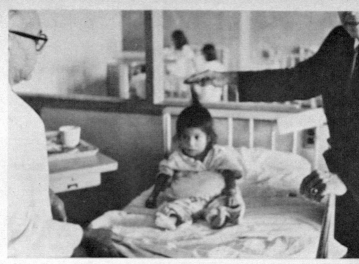

Vivian, to whom this book is dedicated, is six years old and weighs 17 pounds—a victim of malnutrition. Her hair has turned red, one of several evidences of protein deficiency.

Mrs. José Amoedo, a Cuban refugee, registered nurse, and member of the Brother's Brother team, helps feed patients at the Children's Hospital in San José.

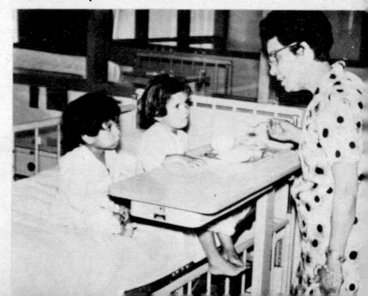

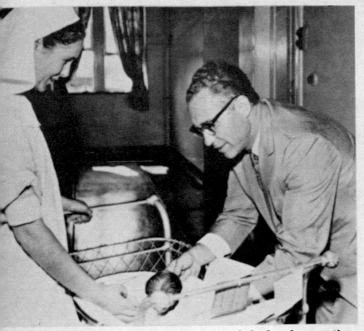

**Dr. Hingson in Australia with a newly born baby for whose mother he has just provided the anesthesia.**

the W.H.O. had in the past seven years practically eliminated this plague in the same country that was now being covered by jet in two months.

The doctors gave a total of 75,000 medical treatments to the ill and performed forty-seven major surgical, obstetrical and dental operations, including sixteen goiters as large as grapefruit, and actually distributed 20 tons of Trinsicon—60 million capsules of iron, vitamins and liver extract.* Throughout it all, they instructed Liberian health officials and medical technicians in the fundamentals of modern health and made suggestions for remedial measures that would remove many causes for disease.

Nor did they overlook other needs of the people. The initial survey had revealed that hundreds of schools had no libraries—not even a single book to lend to interested students. An appeal to American churches, schools, publishers and the like had netted almost 100,000 volumes on law, science, engineering, mathematics, medicine and philosophy. These were distributed, according to subject matter and need, to Liberia's schools. Later Dr. Einar Olsen, a Cleveland Lutheran dentist, inspired Ohio's Kiwanis Clubs to send a second 100,000 books and thus the means of keeping Liberia's schools open for 40,000 children during the austerity budget in 1962-63.

The survey had shown too that much of Liberia's health problem was due to inadequate diet—and that the vegetables needed could be grown in Liberian soil. So a call had gone out from Mrs. Robert Hingson at the written request of Mrs. William Tolbert, a tribal native and educated wife of the vice president, for garden seed. A total of 15,000 pounds of seed was carried on the *Diamond Head* and given to Liberians

* Donated by Eli Lilly & Company.

with instructions on how to grow their own vegetables in 20,000 gardens.

Even after the physicians departed, some U. S. technicians remained to continue inoculation and check results. The vaccinia—evidences of a successful take—looked good, but Dr. Hingson and his colleagues knew that the real test would come a year later. Would the epidemic be repeated?

Dr. Hingson flew back to Africa in 1963 to check Liberia and explore a possible project in Sierra Leone with the secretary of foreign affairs, Dr. John Karefa Smart, now associate director general of the World Health Organization in Geneva. Health authorities told him that the situation was much improved. Rather than the 2,000 cases estimated in 1961, reports had come of only 40 cases—and these were men in remote areas who had not been vaccinated. But statistics are only figures, and Dr. Hingson made his own way to the smallpox hospital where patients had been treated in 120 beds during his visit the year before. He found the building closed and its door locked. He peeped through the windows, and smiled. The 120 cots were folded and stacked against the wall!

It was then that a Liberian male nurse appeared, apparently the caretaker. He remembered the doctor from his efforts a year earlier and anticipated his question. "Thank you, thank you," he smiled. "Smallpox is plenty dead."

Dr. Karl Franz, the medical director of the Firestone Hospital, wrote, "We have not seen a case of smallpox in four months. It has died out in Liberia."

# IX.  A Belt of Immunity
## in Central America

The success of Brother's Brother in Liberia in 1962
was astounding good news. Dr. Hingson was happy
about it, and the Liberian people were happy about it.
Each conveyed their excitement to World Health Organization, and World Health took a hard look at the
results.

Some doctors are naturally and justifiably critical,
and the W.H.O. officials refused to buy all this excitement without thoroughly checking things out for
themselves. They sent their own representative into
Liberia to investigate the claims. Not all reports came
out as happy as Dr. Hingson had reported. One report
came from a physician who attempted to test the jet
gun for himself. He inoculated several hundred persons and got only a 21 per cent take, as contrasted
with the 98 per cent success Brother's Brother had reported. Evidently something was terribly wrong with
one set of statistics!

Unfortunately, this doctor's preliminary statistics
were recorded in a Liberia health report for the year
1963 and given wide circulation among the health
authorities of neighboring nations. The report raised a
serious question as to the use of the jet gun—and as to
the dilution technique. Dr. Hingson estimated that its

publication caused a two-year delay in launching new immunization projects and may have cost thousands of lives. However, it probably saved some too because it demanded careful evaluation and immunologic testing.

Tests need to be tested, and Dr. Hingson appealed to H. Q. Taylor and others in the Liberian health ministry for supporting evidence. This was also expertly provided in a most scientific manner by Drs. Donald Henderson, J. D. Millar and others of the Communicable Disease Center of the U. S. Public Health Service in Atlanta, Georgia.

Two errors had been made in the discouraging calculations: The challenging doctor was, first of all, inexperienced in the use of the jet gun. And secondly, he used outdated vaccine that had lost its medical strength before injection.

Dr. Henderson, with Surgeon General Luther Terry of the U. S. Public Health Service, sent a team of doctors and nurses to the Tonga Islands of the South Pacific—an area about as isolated from modern medicine as he could find anywhere in the world. Sixty-six thousand island residents were immunized against smallpox in a controlled study—with doctors using the jet gun and dilutions of 1 to 10, 1 to 25, 1 to 50, 1 to 100, 1 to 1000 on respective islands 10 to 25 miles apart, exactly as Dr. Hingson had suggested in his reports. When after five days the arms were checked, Dr. Hingson's method received a near-perfect score of 98 per cent. Smaller tests in Brazil and Jamaica had the same happy results.

With these tests now validated, World Health set out to immunize the world's endemic areas. In 1965, the W.H.O. and the U. S. AID program announced plans to vaccinate 105 million people in nineteen African nations against smallpox and measles. And the

W.H.O. announced in 1966 that their teams would move on into Asia as soon as Africa's masses were protected.

The Brother's Brother project in Liberia in 1962 had been a pilot run. Now four years later, Dr. M. G. Candau, the director general of the W.H.O., declared: "Smallpox is one disease that we can now eradicate completely, forever, from the earth."

Against this background, Dr. Henderson approached Dr. Hingson to point out another area of need. The concentration of W.H.O. teams in Africa and Asia left a dreadful health vacuum in the Americas. Would Brother's Brother be willing to do mass immunizations in tropical America similar to the Liberian project?

Dr. Hingson's foundation trustees immediately accepted the challenge.

At least two interesting medical axioms were considered in this decision. Perhaps we should have said theories rather than axioms, because only now were they about to be fully tested.

Health authorities have noted that—for some reason they do not yet explain—no organism, from a microbe to a mammal, can propagate itself once its total numbers fall below a certain point. Disease similarly tends to feed on itself, and when the number of sick is reduced, the percentage of new cases drops even more sharply. An example is the incidence of malaria, which is spread by the bite of mosquitoes. A mosquito bites a malaria patient, then later infects a well person with the parasite. But, the theory says, if the number of ill people drops from 60 per cent to 20 per cent of a population, the mosquito has a greatly reduced likelihood of picking up the disease. If a majority of any population is successfully immunized against disease, the mosquito (or other means of passing the parasite from

one person to another) has an ever-decreasing likelihood of first biting a diseased person and then planting the germ in another who does not already have
immunization!

Such reasoning leads to the conclusion that even
partial vaccination of a country's population will dras-
tically cut the disease toll.

The second theory is related to the first. Disease is
transmitted person to person, or person to insect or
particle of air to person. Distances serve as barriers to
the spread of disease. Oceans have long been effective
walls—until jet aircraft started linking continents in a
matter of a few hours. But even with modern transportation, the spread of disease is halted or slowed by the
absence of new susceptible blood on which it can gain
new strength.

Out of this idea developed the theory of the immunization belt. If a measles epidemic in Panama, for instance, is moving toward Costa Rica, it goes from village to village. But if all the people in an area have
been made immune to the disease through vaccination, the measles germ finds no susceptible person on
which to feed and replenish its kind. The march of the
disease across country has been blocked as effectively
as a moat once stopped attacking armies!

Central America—reaching only a few hundred
miles across from ocean to ocean—was seen as an
effective testing ground. Just as, for instance, the Panama Canal separates the American continents, so an
immunization belt might be built that would prevent
the interchange of disease from countries north and
south of such a line.

Health needs were unquestionably great in the middle American countries of Honduras, Nicaragua and
Costa Rica. Could not the jet gun prove effective in
these lands on both scores: to help rid each country of

its own disease and also construct barriers to block germs coming from other areas?

The idea was considered worth a try. "It's just like fighting a forest fire," one doctor observed. "You build backfires to keep the blazes from crossing designated areas because no brush is left on which it can feed."

# X. Crusade in Honduras

The Brother's Brother idea was to prove as contagious as the diseases it sought to fight. Dr. Hingson told the Liberian Brother's Brother story in a series of five addresses at the 6th Baptist Youth World Conference at Beirut, Lebanon, in July 1963. More than 3,000 heard his lecture. Like the planting of seed, some of his dictums fell on good ground and some on hard. But among those more receptive persons was a young lay leader, Guy Bevil, Jr., of Houston, Texas.

Bevil was youth director for the 1,200-member River Oaks Baptist Church in one of Houston's wealthy suburbs. Once he got back home, his minister invited Dr. Hingson to come and tell the Brother's Brother story to his church and the community.

One journalist who reported the event said: "The congregation at Houston caught fire."

Church members raised funds, secured drugs, and enlisted doctors, nurses, medical students and 200 high-school and college students to meet medical needs wherever they might be found in the middle American republics.

An invitation was soon coming from Dr. José Antonio Peraza, health minister of the Republic of Honduras. Honduras is a land that stood then, and now, in acute need. Its economy was one of the lowest in the Americas. Tropical heat sapped initiative from residents of the lowlands, and steep mountainsides made the inland regions unproductive.

It was also representative of other developing countries of Asia, Africa and Latin America in its dismal incidence of killing and debilitating pestilences.

Dr. Peraza, who gave unlimited cooperation, reported that during the previous year, 1964, hospitals had admitted a total of 81,000 amebiasis patients, 4,600 typhoid cases, 54,000 cases of worms and intestinal cestodes, 4,600 new malaria cases, and 7,650 new cases of tuberculosis. He estimated that at least 50,000 infants and small children die from dysentery each year. Smallpox deaths cannot be recorded accurately, he said; but the observer could tell from the scarring effects on those who survived that this disease was an ever-present threat in a land with too few physicians and health facilities.

Yet, its people loved life, just as did people in all other parts of the world. And they were equally deserving of good health.

The volunteer team of Texans named their group "Amigos de Honduras" (Friends of Honduras) and moved in to give the help they could both in medicine and agrarian reform. And they asked Dr. Hingson to bring along his Brother's Brother experience to get them started.

Traveling by truck, plane, jeep and on foot, the teams of good Samaritans fanned out to create a 50-mile disease immunity belt. An estimated 500,000 shots were needed to do the job.

Their accommodations were adequate in the larger cities, but they found life primitive in remote villages. Yet they asked no special treatment. They slept in rough huts or cabins when such were available—anything in fact that offered shelter from July rains and tropical insects. Chickens and hogs frequently shared the sheds with them, but even this had an advantage: the animals served as alarm clocks to help them get an early start on the next day's work.

Five persons made up each of the many teams that roamed Honduran mountainsides. Each team was headed by a doctor and a nurse. Its other members included technicians and previously untrained volunteers, who readily learned the jet-gun technique after an hour of observation and practice.

Every person coming for vaccination was first registered by the health ministry. His name was recorded, and a billfold-sized certificate was given him for his keeping. From there on it was a rapid-fire procedure. A Boy Scout on either side of the line cleaned the patient's upper arms with a 2-inch paintbrush dipped in antiseptic suds. Next pause was the polio station, where a volunteer technician with a medicine dropper directed vaccine to the back of the tongue. Then the patient stepped between two of the peace guns, simultaneously receiving smallpox vaccine in the left arm and a combination tuberculosis-leprosy (B.C.G.) shot in the right. A fourth person examined each arm as the patient walked away, offering cotton pads to the one in twenty cases where a drop of blood might have been drawn. A registered nurse, meanwhile, stood over a picnic-style ice chest, busily filling sterilized vials with precious medicine for the hungry guns.

Few persons showed evidence of pain when the vaccine was injected. Most registered a surprised smile, their anticipation of pain having proved an unnecessary effort. One seven-year-old barefoot boy took his shots, turned around and grinned as his five-year-old brother got his.

The teams worked fourteen consecutive days without stopping for a single day's rest, and the days were monotonously the same in routine. But they were never monotonous in the minds of the young people and medical men who had set about to bring hope to the children and the parents of Honduras.

Dr. Hingson demonstrated this spirit of perpetual hope and never-tiring zeal in a letter he wrote one night to friends back in Cleveland. It told of his experience on that one eventful day:

"Dr. Pinedas Santos, 33, director of health, and Dr. Gustavo Alvardo, 36, director of tuberculosis control, traveled with me the 30 miles from San Pedro Sula to the village of Progresso. Even as we approached the town we saw a tremendous banner 'Bien Venidos Amigos de Honduras a Progresso' (Welcome Friends of Honduras to Progresso) hanging from the superstructure of a splendid new steel bridge."

The three men turned toward the town square at 1 P.M. in 100-degree heat and saw a seemingly endless line of school children on the railroad tracks. They stood by classes from the first through the ninth grade, and they wore school uniforms of green or white or blue or gray. Each class group was accompanied by its teacher, often but not always a nun or priest. This line of boys and girls extended almost 2 miles to where it reached the health center—wide-eyed expectant youngsters marching toward the "peace gun" their teachers had described.

The doctors drove their car up alongside the line to the new little concrete health center, "and when we got there," Dr. Hingson wrote, "we discovered another line—even longer—coming from another direction. Never in history had our peace gun faced such a challenge: four miles of children, 2,000 to the walking mile."

Dr. Hingson's letter continued its story:

It took ten minutes to press our equipment and iced
vaccine through the crowd. There was the temptation
to stop and pat little boys on the head as their beady
eyes of wonder greeted us and as shy little girls snuggled
closer together. The children won for ten minutes. Their
heads got patted.

No doctor who loves people would be unmoved. I was
immediately aware of our gratitude to Dr. Jenner and
Dr. Koch and Dr. Calmette and Dr. Guerin in medical
history—men who first conceived the vaccines despite the
ridicule and even hostility of their contemporaries. I was
grateful to the American Pharmaceutical Association and
its scientists at Wyeth laboratories in Philadelphia, where
Dr. Tint first made freeze-dried smallpox vaccine from
sacrificial calves. I could in imagination visualize the six
little heifers who suffered and died from cowpox that this
vaccine might be prepared. I was grateful to Lilly and
Lederle and Pfizer and the companies in Japan and Mexico that prepared other valuable doses. I thought also of
friends in Cleveland and New York, Detroit and Pau,
France, who prepared the jet injectors.

All of these people from history and from scattered
parts of today's world had made possible the scene of
which we were a part. Each of them—plus those hundreds of individuals who gave gifts to pay for vaccine
—figuratively stood by our sides as we immunized 7,500
children against two diseases in a single afternoon.

Amigos de Honduras continued through July and
August of 1967, reaching the most remote areas as well
as the towns and cities. Though their personnel was
predominantly Protestant, there was full cooperation
from priests and other authorities of the Roman Catholic Church. When a team of four reached a small village along the Nicaraguan border without advance
publicity, its leader went to the church and told the

priest of their ability to vaccinate against disease. The priest nodded his assent, walked to the bell tower, and rang a hearty call for all the villagers. Some six hundred came to the church and offered their arms to the *pistola de la paz*.

On another occasion, the heat, the dirt and just plain "metal fatigue" caused one jet gun after another to fire sluggishly if at all. But hundreds of hopeful people were waiting, and it would have been tragic to tell them to come back through the Honduran sun another day. An English-speaking priest sensed the tension in the doctor's faces and asked if there was something he could do to help. "Indeed," said Dr. Hingson, "go to the cathedral and pray. These children must be protected in spite of frailty of men or steel." He solemnly gathered six nuns, and off they went to a nearby church. The line only slowed in its march past the guns, as half the team became mechanics on broken *pistolas*. They kept enough in service, replacing the tired ones with those that had been repaired, so that the last brown child walked past the guns as the cathedral clock tolled 6 P.M.

Mrs. Antes, wife of Canton's well-known gynecologist, chose to stay in Tegucigalpa one morning while other members of the team fanned out to rural areas. She asked, however, if there might be some segment of the city's population that she could immunize during the afternoon.

"Yes," a health officer told her, "we've not yet done the men at the prison." Mrs. Antes smiled a bit, then agreed to carry her jet gun there.

It was a bigger assignment than either she or any other member of the Brother's Brother team dreamed. By sundown, with the help of a Honduran nurse, she had vaccinated a total of 2,500 prisoners!

Dr. Hingson returned to Cleveland after two weeks

with the Amigos, but only a few days later Dr. Peraza urged him to fly back to Honduras. The Amigos were concentrating their work in the northwestern part of the country. Dr. Peraza asked Brother's Brother to complete the immunity belt of which he had spoken in their first conversation.

Ralph Hingson had remained in Honduras with the Amigo teams, and Dick Hingson had gone onto Venezuela for two weeks' work with the jets. Upon Dick's return home to Cleveland, he found that his dad was about to leave to help Dr. Peraza build the immunity zone. Without unpacking, Dick was on the plane an hour later for another exciting week in Honduras. Dr. Hingson found on his landing in San Pedro Sula that the sixteen-year-old Ralph had fired 30,000 shots in twenty-two villages in his first sixteen days in the country. On one occasion he walked through 9 kilometers of dusty trail beyond the end of the road to inject 400 in a remote village. On another he used his experience as a track star to run 10 miles for repair parts for a broken gun, making possible the immunization of 1,000 who would have been passed up.

The experience was overwhelming for young Ralph. He identified with the needs of the people and empathized with all he met. One day he became friends with a tubercularly crippled lad in a ragged shirt, and before their conversation ended Ralph and the lad—whose name was Jesus—had traded T-shirts. Young Hingson wrapped the dirty rag carefully in paper and carried it the 2,600 miles to his home in Cleveland Heights—there to hang it on a rack in his room as a reminder of world needs and the help that the world's more developed nations can offer. Then, one night Ralph returned home to find his prized ragged shirt was gone; the maid had thrown it in the incinerator with the trash.

Ralph was quite disturbed over the loss of the shirt, Dr. Hingson recalls. And by breakfast he had penned this poem:

## What Is a Rag?

A rag is a memory,
A piece of misery,
Symbol of a twisted hip,
Inspiration of a mission trip,
The garment of a little boy,
The bearer of which bore no joy
as he hobbled along in agony
and fought the fight against T.B.

"Please, Mother, an operation for my leg?"
"No, we are starving and you must beg."

"Beg, little Jesus, cry for aid.
Your shirt for mine, I'll make a trade.
Now in your little white top, smile for us.
Your shirt I will keep to tell, Jesus,
To tell of hurt, pain, disease,
To plead for you, 'America please.'"

What is a rag?
A piece of cloth, filthy, patched, and rotten,
Burned as trash, but not forgotten.

RALPH HINGSON
*September 1965*

# XI. New Hope in Nicaragua

There was a definite ray of hope in the woman's eyes—a hope hard to understand. There she stood, her bare feet caked with dust, her cotton dress worn and faded. She held a male child in her arms. Two girl children stood by her side.

She and the children had just been vaccinated, without a whimper, against smallpox, tuberculosis and leprosy. The children also had been protected against polio.

The site was the village center of Diriamba in southwestern Nicaragua. More than 300 other Nicaraguans stood in the line for similar jet-gun immunizations being offered for free by a group of United States physicians and other volunteers in cooperation with the Nicaraguan government's health ministry.

"How many children do you have?" Dr. Hingson asked the woman. Six, she answered. He counted uno, dos, tres.

"Two are in the cemetery," she replied. And then nodding to her own stomach she added, "and one is not born yet."

"I have come here," she said, and the hope now shown brightest, "because the radio told me that *pisto-*

*la de la paz* would keep me from having to take other children to the cemetery."

All around us we saw evidences of the ravage of disease. Many had been crippled from smallpox. Many had bloated stomachs, the evidence of worms. Others carried the scars of leprosy. None above sixteen had a full set of teeth. Hacking coughs and slumped shoulders reminded us of the health ministry's estimate that one in every five had tuberculosis.

Only six blocks from the immunization clinic the town cemetery held the bodies of those who had died over the period of a century. Along its back edges were hundreds of wooden crosses, marking the graves of little children—shocking support for statistics that one baby in every two dies before six years of age.

This was one of the scenes during Brother's Brother 1966 health crusade in Nicaragua.

Dr. Hingson and Brother's Brother colleagues had gone this time in a party initiated by youth of the First Baptist Church of Cleveland, where the Hingsons are members. This church, long outstanding in missionary outreach history, had sent its minister, Dr. Francis Wheaton, and Mrs. Wheaton to Liberia in 1962.

Team leader was Dr. Hingson's nominee—a former student of his at Western Reserve University—Dr. Gustavo Parajon, a native of Nicaragua, where his father had served thirty years as pastor of Managua's First Baptist Church. Dr. Parajon had come to the United States for his education, winning Phi Beta Kappa honors with his degrees from both Denison and Western Reserve Universities. And now, 1966, he was chief resident of Cleveland's Metropolitan Hospital.

Dr. Parajon and Dr. Hingson had flown to Managua in May to talk with that country's health chief, Dr. Alfonso Boniche. Dr. Parajon knew the country and its people—and his own lame leg testified as to the results of poliomyelitis on Nicaraguan young people.

The two doctors demonstrated to Nicaraguan officials the efficiency of the *pistola de la paz* by vaccinating 1,000 persons in a single afternoon. It was agreed that Nicaragua would furnish land transportation for the teams, arrange publicity to get a maximum number of people to the vaccination centers, and provide registrar and records.

Hospital Ship *Hope* was anchored at Corinte on the Pacific coast of northern Nicaragua. Dr. Boniche guessed that this ship and its crew would effectively immunize the Pacific area north of Managua. Local health officials could handle the needs in Managua, the capital city. Would the Parajon-Hingson team concentrate, please, on the strip of land west of Lake Nicaragua, running 50 miles wide between the lake and the ocean and 150 miles deep from Managua to the Costa Rican border?

By the time the forty volunteers (including Dr. Hingson's wife and three of his five children) were ready to board planes on July 7, a total of $85,000 in drugs and equipment, including $6,500 from the First Baptist Church, was en route to Nicaragua. Smallpox vaccine was contributed by the Pan American Health Organization. Two thousand dollars came from Baptist Men of Canada. Other contributions came from a cross section of Protestant, Catholic and Jewish organizations in Cleveland and from UNICEF of the United Nations. The polio vaccine came from Canada, B.C.G. (tuberculosis and leprosy) from Japan, and smallpox vaccine from Brazil—thus linking three continents in the venture.

Each member of the team contributed a month of time to the project. Each paid all or part of his own expenses. While in Nicaragua they lived in the homes of the people or slept on the dirt floors of schoolhouses. They cooled their parched throats with iodized water from army canteens and paid little attention otherwise to the sweat that rolled from their bodies under the heat of a Central American sun. One of the youngest of the volunteers, seventeen-year-old Ella Ramsey of Cleveland, typified their dedication as she stood hour after hour dropping polio vaccine on the tongues of open-mouthed children. Her brown hair hung in her face, a splotch of black grime covered one cheek, her fancy black lace slip drooped an inch and a half below the hem of her blue denim dress. Her face showed a single concern: to save these youngsters from the disease that already had crippled or killed many of their playmates.

Roger Newton, a student at the University of Virginia, putt-putted his way on a Honda cycle into Managua, one of several planned stops on a leisurely summer tour of Latin America. But he met Dr. Hingson in a hotel courtyard and listened to the Brother's Brother story. He parked his Honda with the hotel management and spent the next two weeks pushing the trigger of a jet gun!

Nicaragua also marked a milestone for Albert Burroughs, the Negro orderly of Cleveland's University Hospitals who had come along to dismantle, clean and repair the jet guns every night, and who had insisted on giving immunizations as well. During a several months' stay in Liberia in 1962, he had immunized 90,000 persons; he ran his total past 100,000 in the first ten days in Nicaragua.

Another Negro, the Reverend John T. Weeden, president of the Cleveland Baptist Pastors Conference, performed similarly heroic work. He came to view the mission aspects of the Brother's Brother program; he became so concerned with need that he eagerly learned to shoot the jet gun and stood first in line for every difficult assignment.

For several weeks radio, newspapers, posted bulletins, sound trucks and word of mouth had told the people of the coming of Brother's Brother. The signs, "Hermanos de los Hermanos," were posted by the Nicaraguan Ministry of Health as profusely as an advance man's work for the Barnum and Bailey Circus.

The radio—and every Nicaraguan has a radio receiver whether or not he can buy shoes for his feet— told of *pistola de la paz,* a gun of peace that could drive disease from their homes. And this *pistola de la paz* was unique because it injected vaccine without a needle.

Great crowds of Nicaraguans came to village vaccination centers, and sometimes as many as 400 stood in line by the time the medical team arrived at 8 A.M. On mountainsides the people gathered at announced hours at preselected coffee haciendas. They met at crossroads in the valleys, and they paddled canoes to island clinics in Lake Nicaragua's thousand-island area. One Indian woman came astride a donkey, one child in her arms, three more children on the animal's rump behind her, and a fifth child hanging onto the donkey's mane.

One grimy-faced man clearly showed his pre-shot apprehension. "Will it hurt me to be vaccinated after two drinks?" he asked the doctor. The doctor smiled and assured him the two drinks would not cause any bad effects from the shot. And then the man surprised him with: "I'll be back in a few minutes after I've had two drinks."

There was evidence too that the Nicaraguans considered this visit by the *Norteamericanos* a Sunday-go-to-meeting occasion. Most women wore their best clothes. A doctor withheld his gun from one teen-aged girl when he recognized her bright blue dress with a white embroidered cross as one which had been through the line a few minutes earlier. "I cannot vaccinate you again," he told the girl. To which she replied, "I have not been here before." When he mentioned the dress, she explained that her sister had worn the dress through the line earlier and then brought it back home so she could wear it. An hour later the dress came through the line a third time.

People were not so affluent in other locations. Dr. Hingson and I walked the length of the waiting line in one of the villages, Diriamba. Of the 104 persons in the line only 40 wore shoes.

We also found the people in great need of dental care. We looked into the mouths of a hundred persons one afternoon, to learn that not a single person past fourteen had a full set of teeth. The diet of pineapple and other sweet fruit, plus the lack of dental hygiene, caused massive decay at the gum line.

Dr. Hingson had anticipated this problem and invited five advanced students from the Baylor University School of Dentistry to join the team. While jet guns did their work in one area, these dentists performed oral surgery on 688 persons, removing 1,650 diseased teeth.

Apparently most of the 130,000 who received shots during the three weeks Brother's Brother was in Nicaragua were grateful. One woman who brought her two children to a rural station disappeared into the bush and returned moments later with freshly plucked bananas for each of her benefactors.

But the prime compliment came when Nicaraguans at the historic town of Granada expressed their appreciation with a barbecue on the final day of vaccinations in that area. "Go back to America and tell your government that we don't want any more of your dollars," said the mayor, Dr. Luis Urbina Naguera. "We want people like you to come blend your sweat with our sweat to cure our nation's problems."

# XII. A Health Resource Pool for Central America

Brother's Brother had been pledged to cooperate with youth of the First Baptist Church in Cleveland again in 1967, protecting four districts in Nicaragua they had not reached in 1966. But the mission committee of the church notified Dr. Hingson in early May that they felt capable of handling the Nicaraguan venture alone, and the Brother's Brother team would be free to work elsewhere.

Dr. Hingson and other trustees immediately prepared a letter offering their services to the health ministries of eleven republics in Central America and along the northern edge of the South American continent.

## Emergency in Costa Rica

Dr. Alvaro Aguilar Peralta, minister of health for the Republic of Costa Rica, was the first to respond. He sent Dr. Hingson a telegram Wednesday, June 7, asking him to come to San José to talk about a saturation campaign to immunize his country's 1½ million people. Airmail letters came from Dr. J. Antonio Peraza, minister of health for the Republic of Honduras, and from Dr. Abraham Pretto, the minister of health in Panama, and later a cable from Ecuador.

By Friday, June 9, a team of eight was organized and ready to leave the following Tuesday. Then on Sunday, a second telegram came from Dr. Aguilar. Measles was epidemic in Costa Rica, he said, and the mortality rate was almost 9 out of every 100 cases. Please come immediately, he said, bringing 75,000 doses of measles vaccine for the school children of San José.

The Brother's Brother Foundation trustees met in emergency session on Sunday night, and instructed Dr. Hingson to try to find the requested vaccine at the best possible price. Departure date was moved from Tuesday to Friday to permit time for acquisition of the additional medicine.

Twenty telephone calls and two days later, Dr. Hingson had only 700 rather than 75,000 doses of vaccine. This had come through the special services of Dr. Harry C. Helm of Columbia, Tennessee, who borrowed it from the Tennessee Department of Health. Peter Noble of the Pharmaceutical Manufacturers Association in Washington canvassed manufacturers and found all but one, Pitman-Moore, in short supply. And that company, as were others, was giving first attention that week to meeting emergency Red Cross needs in the Israeli-Arab war.

The eight team members climbed aboard jet aircraft in Cleveland, Washington, Nashville, and Houston Friday morning June 16—set to rendezvous in El Salvador to finish the trip on to San José together. They were Dr. Hingson and his son Ralph, Dr. Antes, Dr. and Mrs. José Amoedo, Dr. Harry C. Helm, and Mr. Robert F. Miller of the Cleveland Trust Company. I was also a member of the party. Drs. Hingson, Antes, Helm and the Amoedoes were veterans in mass immunization campaigns. Miller had joined the group as business advisor—having become interested in Dr.

Hingson's idealism through his reading of a news article by UPI columnist Louis Cassels in the *Cleveland Press.*

They carried a maximum amount of baggage aboard the planes. Together they had 38 inoculators, 30,000 doses of smallpox vaccine, 2,000 influenza shots, some tetanus and typhoid vaccines, and the much-sought-after 700 doses of measles vaccine. The medicine, packed in dry ice, was carried aboard the passenger compartment to guarantee its safety from tropical heat.

Dr. Aguilar, three other health ministry representatives and U. S. AID representative Albert Grego met the Pan American plane when it landed in San José the night of June 16. Dr. Hingson told them of our inability to get necessary measles vaccine on short notice.

Further news arrived by cable during the night, however. Fifty thousand doses of measles vaccine were available from Pitman-Moore for $1.10 per dose. This was a tremendous reduction in cost from the commercial $2.95 per dose, but it still called for $55,000. The needed 75,000 doses would require $82,500, and even this would care for only the children in San José. (Yet Pitman-Moore had faith and compassion too and gave ninety days' credit, and later after 10 per cent payment allowed another ninety days.)

Thus, while the news gave our group new hope, the problem was still a long way from solution.

Costa Rica is a beautiful tropical land of 1,433,000 persons living in an area of 23,421 square miles, about the size of West Virginia. It is the southern-most of the Central American republics sitting on a 300-mile-wide ocean to ocean strip just north of Panama and south of Nicaragua. Despite its tropical location, an interior plateau on which San José, the capital, is located is about 4,000 feet above sea level and enjoys cool nights.

The country is unique among nations of the world because it has no armed forces except for a Guardia Civil (national guard) of fewer than 2,000 members. It spends a higher percentage of its budget on health and education than any other country of the Western Hemisphere. This is reflected in its culture, architecture and the arts. Yet in this land of eternal summers, disease germs find an optimum environment.

At the health ministry offices Saturday morning, Dr. Miguel Angel Cortés reported that measles had killed 1,516 children in Costa Rica (reported cases) the year before, and that an estimated 10,000 children were suffering from the disease at the present time. He cited that tropical conditions and malnutrition contribute to a high mortality rate. He said also that only 40 per cent of the Costa Rican people had been immunized against diphtheria, whooping cough or tetanus (D.P.T. vaccine), only 60 per cent against polio, and 20 per cent against smallpox. Polio and smallpox, reported in Nicaragua to the north and Panama to the south, were a constant threat.

Dr. Hingson unpacked his bags on a table in the center of the room and neatly laid out one weapon after another. He demonstrated the Western Reserve gas machine, explaining its usefulness for anesthesia in surgery and for oxygen in heart and respiratory illness. "We want to leave this machine with you, and we want to give another to the Children's Hospital," he said.

He next demonstrated three different models of the peace gun. Pointing a Press-o-jet toward the ceiling, he fired distilled water into the air. A thousand particles sprayed forth—his listeners were convinced. Then he inserted a vial of influenza vaccine and fired a shot into the arm of Dr. José Amoedo, one of the Brother's Brother team members. One by one the roomful of spectators offered their arms for treatment. And a news photographer who came by for a picture assignment got his dose too.

Dr. Rodrigo Jimenez Monge, chief of epidemiology, explained that a comprehensively planned program—already mimeographed and bound—was no good in the absence of measles vaccine. He suggested that the team members spend the weekend sightseeing, while he prepared a new program to fit the available supplies.

On Monday, there were still further conferences. Dr. Hingson's son, Ralph, was anxious to start using the guns on the field and whispered to the author that the Latins apparently are as much afflicted as North Americans with *trámites burocráticos* or red tape. We were to learn later in the week that the health officials were simply stalling for time while they sought money to pay their part of the cooperative effort.

By Tuesday, however, six inoculation clinics were at work. Drs. Hingson, Antes, Amoedo and Helm, Nurse Amoedo and Technician Ralph Hingson each headed a team to give smallpox vaccine to 30,000 children in the San José schools. Two Costa Rican nurses accompanied each team leader. The youngsters found the clinics a major innovation in the class routine, as the doctors went from desk to desk giving shots with the magic pistol.

Tuesday afternoon, AID representative Grego took team members to the American Embassy so they could tell their story to Ambassador Clarence A. Boonstra. Would it be possible, they asked, to get American help in financing vaccines and arranging transportation? Mr. Boonstra promised to do his best.

Meanwhile, the Brother's Brother representatives

and Drs. Aguilar, Jiminez and Cortés had worked out a plan for eighty-five North American doctors, nurses and technicians to return to Costa Rica on August 1 to immunize all the country's residents. Additional measles vaccine would be available by that time. They optimistically planned that at least 1 million persons would receive protection from smallpox, tuberculosis and leprosy; 300,000 children would also be protected against measles and polio. Dr. Hingson knew that smallpox and polio vaccines were available from the Pan American Health Organization on Dr. Aguilar's request. The Baptist World Alliance offered to give a $1,300 electric power gun, and the Pan American Health Organization to give a power gun and eighteen of the hand-operated Dermo-jets. But more than $300,000 would be needed in cash to pay for measles vaccine. Another $50,000 was needed for supporting equipment. Dr. Aguilar said that Costa Rica could furnish personnel support in doctors, nurses and technicians and also would provide in-country transportation for the team. The question of $350,000 financial support still hung in the balance.

Meanwhile, we paid a visit to one of the evidences of Costa Rica's concern for health, the completely modern Hospital de los Niños—Children's Hospital—in San José. It was designed by medical advisors in the U. S. AID program and was financed by the Smathers Foundation of Florida. The building cost $2 million, and equipment brought the overall expenditure to $3.5 million.

As mentioned in Chapter I, Dr. C. Saenz Herrara, former vice president and director of the hospital, reported a total of 525 patients being treated in 460 beds the day we visited—meaning that 65 beds had two patients each. One is instantly impressed with Dr. Saenz' love for children, and the youngsters greeted him with smiles and admiration. When we visited with Vivian, six years old and weighing a bare 17 pounds, her smile was cheerful, although her diminutive size, the redness in her hair and her swollen stomach told us she was a victim of malnutrition. Scores of the youngsters had a protein deficiency, caused by a diet of too much starch. Yet—and I could not get away from this impression—the children were happy. Even those who had gone through surgery and those suffering from tropical diseases smiled and greeted the strangers entering their rooms. Apparently they were being shown more personal care and being fed better food than they had ever known before. Some of them, doctors said, had never slept on a bed before coming to the hospital.

President José Joaquín Trejos of the Costa Rican Republic invited the team to his office on Wednesday —apparently to hear for himself the full story Dr. Aguilar had already outlined. Dr. Amoedo, Dr. Aguilar and President Trejos discussed in Spanish the needs and the potential benefits of a nation-wide crusade. Dr. Hingson explained the gun's qualities for mass immunization and again outlined plans for the August crusade, with emphasis on financial need.

Cordiality and hope were evident as the team left. But during the afternoon, the President told Dr. Aguilar that though he had tried every possible source of funds he could not find money in the budget to support the crusade.

The health minister was almost in tears that evening when he came to the hotel to tell Hingson of his country's financial difficulties and the apparent necessity that plans for the crusade be terminated.

Dr. Hingson had faced similar crises before. "America is interested in the health and the welfare of the children of Costa Rica," he said. "We will go back to the States and appeal to our friends for the money. We cannot let $300,000 stand in the way of this project."

Then, shaking the health minister's hand, he said: "Get everything ready for us just as we had planned. We'll have eighty-five people here on August first."

Dr. Hingson phoned the Pitman-Moore Company to send vaccine and charge it to him personally. Then he flew on, the next day, to Panama, and thence to Ecuador, Nicaragua and Honduras. But for the sake of the story, let us now continue our attention to Costa Rica.

Once the team returned to Cleveland, Robert F. Miller, vice president of Cleveland Trust Company, prepared a booklet of Xeroxed materials in an appeal to American foundations for money to finance the Costa Rican project. Many small gifts came, but few large ones. Dr. John Cleland of Oregon wrote that his health would prevent his going but he wanted to pay the air fare for some volunteer. A church in Alabama sent a special plate collection of $67. Things still looked difficult—until miracles started happening.

Within a single week, Dr. Hingson learned these things: Dr. Abraham Horwitz of the Pan American Health Organization phoned that he had learned through tests in Chile that a certain type of measles vaccine could be diluted 1 to 5 in the jet gun. The vaccines already ordered would now be fully adequate. Dr. Aguilar cabled that the Costa Rican government, by extraordinary measures, had found $50,000 to put into the project. And he said too that Lacsa, the Costa Rican airline, would fly eighty-three members of the team from Miami to San José at cost—a saving estimated at $12,000.

And thus, as in Liberia, a crisis had ended in a miracle! On August 1, the volunteer team walked aboard the Lacsa plane in Miami and flew to Costa Rica. For the next four weeks, these volunteers joined Costa Rica health personnel in traveling by single-engine plane, jeep, oxcart, boat and on foot to every area of the country where people live. They immunized 843,000 persons and performed other medical services.

The main team flew back to the States on August 30, but Wilbert Tucker, a Cleveland hospital orderly, stayed behind working with Costa Ricans who had learned the vaccination technique . . . and the goal of 1 million seemed assured. "We have saved at least a thousand young children from certain death," Dr. Hingson said.

An epidemic had been averted, but financial problems remained. Brother's Brother still owed more than $80,000 on vaccines, $3,400 on guns, and additional bills for a total of $101,000. Many expected gifts from American industry had failed to materialize. However, Pitman-Moore and Merck Sharp & Dohme, as examples of the philanthropic pharmaceutical industry, accepted 10 per cent payment gathered from churches and agreed on an additional six months' credit for vaccines they sold below cost in the first place.

"It is unfortunate that we have the word 'Foundation' in our name," said Dr. Hingson. "It makes people think we have a lot of money when in fact we stay broke all the time."

## Polio in Nicaragua

The most exciting, most dramatic portion of the June 1967 exploratory trip was unscheduled and unexpected. Dr. Hingson and Ralph Hingson had been to Guayaquil and Quito, Ecuador, laying groundwork for crusades there in 1968 and 1969. They came back via Panama, and while waiting for connections at the airport in the early morning hours they visited with Dr.

Abraham Horwitz of the P.A.H.O., who was en route from Chile to Washington.

The TACA plane carrying the Hingsons had just taken off from Tocumen airport, which serves Panama City and Balboa, when Dr. Hingson read in a morning newspaper about a raging poliomyelitis epidemic in Nicaragua. It was an epidemic of international significance, threatening to close the doors of commerce between Nicaragua and its neighbors. Polio, with its tremendous damage to the respiratory system, is a disease which especially beckons to the skill of anesthesiologists. Dr. Hingson himself had been a mighty force in combating an epidemic in his home city of Cleveland in 1953.

The tragedy now enveloping Nicaragua tugged at the doctor's heart. He signaled for a stewardess and told her he wanted to land at Managua. She explained their plane was headed for Tegucigalpa, not for Managua. But at his insistence she relayed his request to the plane's captain, Jim Law, who invited him to the cockpit.

Dr. Hingson told the pilot of his own experience in treating polio cases, and explained the epidemic raging in Managua. "I can save lives if you will put me down there," he said. Captain Law agreed dubiously to radio for permission to change his flight plan and to ask for landing rights in Managua.

Within moments, Managua responded to the request. "Dr. Hingson needed and welcomed," the terse ministry of health message stated.

Then as the TACA plane made its unscheduled landing (Captain Law is known in aeronautical circles as "God's Errand Boy"), airport officials rushed to the plane on government instructions, took Dr. Hingson's baggage directly to a waiting limousine—skipping immigration and customs delays—and whisked him to the health ministry. The country's new vice president and health minister, Dr. Francisco Urcuyo Maliaños, greeted him with a Latin embrace and led him immediately to conferences with other health officials including the sweet-spirited Dr. Miguel Sequiera A., with whom the Brother's Brothers had worked so closely in 1966.

The epidemic had already grown to 192 known cases, with more than 120 in Managua, they told him. Only 60 of these cases could be accommodated in the hospital. Fourteen had already died. Others were gasping their last breaths because not enough respirators could be found. Five children were under one large improvised plastic oxygen tent on one adult bed. Dr. Hingson went from bed to bed, consulting with local doctors and suggesting medications, tracheotomies, and other treatment as seemed wise.

The pace continued for six days. Dr. Urcuyo shared his office with his American benefactor. The American chargé-d'affaires, James B. Engele, loaned him a car and chauffeur. Señora Hope Somoza, Secretary of Social Security and sister-in-law of the late president Luis Somoza Debayle, asked Dr. Hingson to confer with her and U. S. AID representatives to outline the need for combating the spread.

By July 1, the illness toll had climbed to 271 cases, 26 were dead and a total of 682 extremities—an average of almost 3 per person—were paralyzed, but new respirators and other equipment had been flown in and were cutting down the death rate. In his role as chairman of the Relief Committee of the World Federation of Societies of Anesthesiologists, Dr. Hingson phoned three men he thought best trained to battle the epidemic and asked them to fly to Managua. All three came. These, making up the first of two teams which were to alleviate the emergency, were Dr. Rob-

ert Smith of Harvard University and director of anesthesia at Boston Children's Hospital, Dr. Manuel
Guerrero of the Moline, Illinois, Public Hospital, and
Dr. Christen Rattenborg, associate professor of anesthesiology at the University of Chicago. Dr. Guerrero
is a native of Spain and Dr. Rattenborg a native of
Denmark, giving the project a truly international
flavor.

Hospital interns had, tragically, picked the emergency as an opportune time to call a strike for better
working conditions. This spurred Dr. Hingson to work
even harder to train nurses and other personnel on the
finer points he had learned from his 1953 experience in
Cleveland. He called one chubby Negro nurse to the
side of a new McKesson oxygen tent and asked her to
place a baby inside. He showed her how to adjust the
flow of gases—the first time she had ever used oxygen
in her nursing experience. She smiled and thanked him
for his help. The patient, less than two years old,
smiled too as he began to breathe more easily.

It was Sunday morning and Dr. Hingson had stayed
almost steadily for six days in the hospital wards. Dr.
Sequiera put his arm around Hingson's waist in a
show of appreciation.

"Other doctors went to church," Dr. Sequiera philos-
ophized. "You remained with our babies. The church
is not sick. Our babies are very sick. Nicaragua will
not forget."

Another note needs to be added to the story. The
1966 immunization campaign by Brother's Brother
had been concentrated along the 50-mile-wide and
150-mile-long strip of land south of Managua and west
of Lake Nicaragua. The team had not worked in Managua. The box score in the epidemic showed 17 cases
in the immunized strip; 170 in the city of Managua.

Dr. Hingson flew back to the States late in the after-

noon of July 3 in an effort to mobilize American resources in sending medical equipment and vaccine to
the stricken nation. He wrote:

> Ten cents worth of vaccine, each drop properly in-
> stalled on the tongues of these 471 afflicted children,
> would have prevented a $10,000,000 epidemic which
> leaves cripples dragging useless limbs across Nicaraguan
> streets for another 60 years.
>
> I believe that the 105 American industries with a profit
> motive in Nicaragua will join with the churches in re-
> sponding to this need. A nation with interests strong
> enough to send Marines when this country was threat-
> ened can certainly send vaccines.

That his work was appreciated even by Americans
in Nicaragua was demonstrated in a cable reaching
him in Cleveland July 8:

> On behalf of Embassy I wish express great apprecia-
> tion for your splendid assistance to Nicaragua and wise
> counsel to us during critical period of polio crisis here
> early this month, as well as our admiration your effort to
> mobilize U. S. private resources. . . .
>
> There are now sufficient personnel, lungs and respira-
> tors (at least 15) and vaccine for special national vacci-
> nation program beginning July 9. Since medical opinion
> is that current crisis will shortly be under control, atten-
> tion is now beginning to shift to rehabilitation and sec-
> ond round vaccinations next month.
>
> Nicaraguan radio has been voicing gratitude to you and
> First Baptist Church of Ohio and yesterday morning's
> newspaper "Novedades" front paged an article entitled
> "American Physician Undertakes Crusade to Help Nic-
> aragua."
>
> Many thanks and may your efforts continue to be
> fruitful.
>
> JAMES B. ENGELE
> *Chargé D'affaires*

*New Plans in Panama*

While Drs. Hingson, Antes and Helm were complet-
ing arrangements for the August crusade in Costa
Rica, four members of the June 1967 party—Dr. and
Mrs. Amoedo, Mr. Miller and I—flew on to Panama
City to initiate conversations with the health ministry
there.

Though the letter of invitation was signed by Dr.
Abraham Pretto, the Minister of Labor, Public Health
and Social Welfare, our conversations were to be with
Dr. Alberto Calvo, the Director of Public Health. A
telephone call early Thursday morning brought the request, "Come immediately." Dr. Calvo and four of his
assistants were waiting for the group, and for an hour
they listened attentively as Dr. Amoedo told the
Brother's Brother story and demonstrated the magic
jet inoculator.

There was no need for a discussion of health needs
in the country, for Dr. Calvo himself said that "Outside the Panama City vicinity and the area adjacent to
the canal, there is no doubt that our health situation is
a disgrace. Our problem is lack of resources at the
local level."

Dr. Calvo said further: "We have faith in your machines and a great admiration and appreciation for
your group. I am convinced that with your help we
have a chance to do what we need to do."

Another Panamanian health official said that
measles is killing whole communities in some parts of
the Indian population.

It was proposed that a demonstration of the vaccine
program be conducted in a strip of Panama where a
new canal has been proposed. This section has a population of about 20,000, most of them Indians. It is inac-
cessible except by helicopter or burro from the rest of

the country, and the people need protection against smallpox, syphilis, measles, polio, tuberculosis and leprosy.

Dr. Hingson arrived on the next day to participate in a second conference with Dr. Calvo and his associates. "We have not come here to do a job *for* you; we have come here to do a job *with* you," he said. Arrangements were made for a group of five representatives from Brother's Brother Foundation to come to Panama in the fall to demonstrate their program in this area, with the thought that further projects will be planned for 1968.

When the conferences were over, Dr. Hingson observed that the Panama project will be another in the chain of events fulfilling the Brother's Brother objective: "To share our abundant health resources and ourselves with our developing nations in a full-scale attack upon remedial disease problems in the broadest base of human cooperation."

"A new U. S. image is thus developing," he penned in a letter to friends at home. "Man speaks to man only after his deeds of service provide a podium for expression of new friendship."

## Evaluation of the Summer

The summer of 1967 had definitely taken its place with the summers of 1958 and 1962 as a significant date for innovations in world health.

The survey of 1958 had alerted both churchmen and medical men to the tremendous challenges facing them in the world-wide fight against disease. The smallpox crusade in Liberia in 1962 had demonstrated the effectiveness of the jet gun and its surprising ability to use diluted vaccine.

Now, 1967 realistically demonstrated to all Central

America the wisdom of mass immunization campaigns. A threatened disastrous poliomyelitis epidemic
had been nipped in Nicaragua, and an outbreak of
measles had been quelled in Costa Rica. Dr. Hingson's
hope for a 50-mile immunization zone coast to coast
across the isthmus was not only realized—it was tripled to reach 150 miles from Nicaragua to Panama. Invitations for future campaigns came from the governments of Panama and Ecuador.

Health ministers of the Central American Republics
made plans to establish a "bank" of immunization
equipment and vaccine at San José—a city almost exactly midway between the borders of Colombia and
Mexico. When it is fully equipped, massive protection
measures can be launched in any Central American
country almost immediately after a health minister an-
ticipates an outbreak of contagious disease. Planes can
bring help to the most distant point in less than two
hours.

In eventful hours of mass sickness and death in
many neighbor nations, the Brother's Brother Foundation members gave every available resource—more
than a million-dollar value on two fronts simultaneously. Brother's Brother was the major factor in
stopping polio in Nicaragua and measles in Costa Rica.
In a letter to Dr. Hingson, C. A. Boonstra, United
States Ambassador to the Republic of Costa Rica,
wrote the following evaluation:

It was a pleasure to meet you and members of your
Foundation and to have had the opportunity to participate in several vaccination sessions.

Judging by the over-all results obtained, there is no
question but that your program was indeed successful.
The campaign, of course, conferred tremendous benefits
on this country in the protection it has afforded the great

majority of the population against serious diseases which previously took a heavy toll of lives and money. In addition, the campaign has immeasurably strengthened the bonds of friendship and goodwill between Costa Rica and our country.

Enclosed are copies of correspondence exchanged with Dr. Manuel Angel Cortés, who clearly feels as I do.

I sincerely wish you and your Foundation all possible success in your humanitarian efforts. Your Foundation deserves its name.

Sincerely,

C. A. BOONSTRA
*Ambassador*

# XIII.  A Sick World Made Well

The *Washington Post* ran the story under a two-column headline on December 31, 1966: "Eradication of Smallpox Seen in Next Ten Years."

It was a happy announcement of the beginning of realization of the World Health Organization's plan to drive this pestilential disease from the earth, one of the most ambitious programs ever attempted for human welfare.

W.H.O. leaders had been convinced, following Dr. Hingson's pilot project in Liberia in 1962, that the jet gun might hold the answer to the world's health problems. His success in vaccinating whole villages in a few hours and his theory on 1-to-10 dilution of vaccine was nothing short of startling. It represented vast savings in both time and finances.

The W.H.O. was convinced of the possibility but skeptical of the reality. Their doctors ran their own tests for three years in the Tonga Islands, in Jamaica and in Brazil.

Their findings satisfactory, leaders proposed a world-wide smallpox eradication program at the 18th World Health Assembly in 1965. President Johnson responded by pledging the United States' willingness "to work with other interested countries to see to it that smallpox is a thing of the past by 1975."

The W.H.O. completed its plans within the year, and by its 1966 meeting had sufficient funds and personnel to launch the ten-year program. Jet guns loaded with smallpox vaccine started firing almost immediately in eighteen African countries. A similar program is under way in crowded Asia.

This was the story that writer Alfred Friendly told in the *Washington Post*. He cited the death toll of smallpox through the ages—it was partially responsible for the fall of the Roman Empire; it paved the way to Spanish conquest of Mexico by killing 3 million natives. Again and again it had struck, killing 14,000 Parisians and 18,000 residents of Iceland in 1707. It killed 3 million Indians in 1770. It has recurred frequently in recent years, fortunately without such great tolls—but the peril is a constant threat.

The World Health Organization had been encouraged by discovery of the law of nature that no organism can propagate itself once its total numbers fall below some critical figure. Unless the population of anything, from microbe to mammal, is large enough, it will die.

Vaccinations against smallpox had already removed it as a critical threat in North America, and the belief persisted that mass vaccinations in Asia and Africa could wipe it from the world. And mass immunization was now possible, W.H.O. officials believed, because of two developments. One was the large-scale production of a dry vaccine which remains stable in tropical countries. The other was the jet gun and the dilution technique.

Once smallpox is conquered, similar programs are envisioned to eradicate other diseases, one by one. The pace may actually be doubled or tripled, as vac-

cine combinations are introduced, and as programs are
initiated to give vaccines simultaneously in both arms
as Dr. Hingson has done in his Central American crusades.

## Many Other Needs

No man deceives himself into believing that the
healthy world we dream about will result by magic.
Nor will it happen overnight with even the hardest
work. Accomplishment of the W.H.O.'s definition of
health as being a person's "total and physical well-being" cannot be legislated. Nor can it come into being
solely by the giving of vaccinations.

The causes of disease, the causes of unhappiness,
the causes of human unrest on both personal and community levels must be eliminated. Agricultural methods which have brought about food surpluses in North
America must be made a part of the economy of all
nations. Sanitary engineering is imperative in the villages, towns and cities throughout the world. People
must be educated into healthy hygiene (Dr. Alfredo
Bica, director of epidemiology for the Pan American
Health Organization, says: "We can build latrines all
over the world, but they are useless until people are
educated to use them"). Also imperative is a development of personal motivation—a sense of self-respect
and self-ambition—in the peoples of the world.

Freedom from disease, sought by Dr. Hingson with
the meager resources of the Brother's Brother team,
must be multiplied by the W.H.O. and supported by
John Doe, with immunization as a keystone to the
program. For unless a man is well in body, he is crippled in every other phase of life.

Peoples of the developing nations face dozens of
other needs as well. The United Nations, the United

States Agency for International Development, and agencies within separate continents are at work to apply modern skills to agriculture, commerce, sanitation and general economy in the developing nations. Adults are being taught useful occupations, children are being educated—all in the belief that these peoples and these nations can someday be self-sustaining.

Just as these economic advances depend upon the freedom from disease, continued good health is conversely dependent upon good agriculture and a constructive economy.

## The Problem of Overpopulation

Already the death rate has fallen sharply. The people of India, for instance, had an average life expectancy of twenty-seven as recently as 1920; now the average Indian expects to live to the age of fifty. The country's annual death rate fell from 31 per thousand in 1940 to 16 per thousand in 1966. Latin America's death rate has dropped even more sharply—to 13 per thousand.

The falling death rate has coincided with a rising birth rate so that a new problem has developed in both health care and world economy—overpopulation.

India had 500 million people in 1967, as compared with 340 million in 1947. The population of Latin America was 195 million in 1961, had jumped to 245 million in 1967, and is expected to reach 700 million in the year 2000 unless birth control methods are made effective.

The falling death rate is, of course, applauded, because we have the natural instinct to hold onto life for ourselves and all others. Rising birth rates are a much more controversial subject. The Roman Catholic Church stands firm against use of contraceptive devices, believing that life is a gift from God and that God himself has the right to determine whether a child is born. Other groups, considering their view just as sacred and humane, contend that parents are at fault in bringing a child into the world unless they can guarantee that child proper care and education.

Dr. Hingson took a suitcase filled with intra-uterine loops with him to Honduras in 1965. He left the bag closed until the day before his scheduled departure because he was fully conscious of the Roman Church's teaching against contraceptives. But as time neared for him to leave, he spoke to a village doctor in whose office he was working about the contraceptives and asked if the physician knew any woman patients whose life might be endangered by future pregnancies. The doctor did not answer. Late that afternoon, however, the doctor brought a woman to Dr. Hingson and explained that he believed future pregnancies were unwise for her.

Dr. Hingson opened his bag and explained to the Honduran doctor how the loop should be applied. They explained to the woman what they had done.

Within an hour a line of village women made their way to the doctor's office. The first mother had told her secret. Dr. Hingson's bag was empty when he left Honduras next day.

The story stands as an indication that parents, perhaps everywhere, are disturbed in their inability to care properly for large families. They welcome help in family planning. And this desire conceivably will break down the cultural barriers that have so long blocked introduction of birth-control measures in India, Latin America and many other countries.

An International Planned Parenthood Federation already is working in eighty-seven nations to provide information and contraceptive devices to mothers who want planned families.

"The goal is not just fewer people," said Dr. Leona Baumgartner of the U. S. State Department. "It is to give greater opportunity to all for a fuller life—a chance for freedom from hunger, disease, ignorance and poverty, for development of their own innate capacities, and for helping their children.

"To achieve these goals, many people want smaller families. Effective methods are available. Their widespread application comes next."

## A Continuing Story

Achievement of a healthy world is, as we said, a continuing story. But we can happily take courage that vast advances are being made. The incidence of cholera, typhoid, malaria, tuberculosis, and leprosy is definitely on the wane. New world-wide programs for elimination of disease-carrying mosquitoes are under way.

Vast new programs of research into the causes and cures of cancer and heart disease are being undertaken cooperatively by the 126 nations in the World Health Organization. Already the W.H.O. has learned that cancer, which kills more than 2 million persons a year, appears in many forms, and its geographical distribution is unequal. Cancer of the breast is much rarer in Japan than in most countries. Cancer of the liver, which is rare in Europe and North America, accounts for more than half the cancer deaths among the Bantu in Africa. When the reasons for these geographical or sociological differences becomes known, perhaps a cure will be in sight.

We asked Dr. Hingson to summarize the most significant advances in world health, as he sees them, since his survey trip into Asia and Africa ten years ago. This is his analysis:

1. The number of patients suffering from malaria has been reduced by 50 per cent. This is a tribute to the unrelenting emphasis and attack of the World Health Organization in partnership with the nations against the influence of this scythe of the populations. Whole islands, such as Ceylon in the Indian Ocean, and desert-locked lands such as Iran in the Middle East, have been almost freed from this disease through effective spray programs, continuous vigilance and clearing of the human reservoirs through effective therapy.

2. The dreaded white plague of tuberculosis is being controlled in both the developing and the developed countries through better diet, therapy and improvement of the socio-economic housing, ventilation and heating around the world. In some instances hospitals formerly filled to capacity are now half vacant and are being converted for other health uses.

3. Poliomyelitis is a disease which no longer has a reason to exist, with the near-perfect Sabin vaccine which can be dropped on the tongue with two spaced trivalent doses. The United States, which recorded many epidemics until as recently as 1956 and 1957, reported only fifteen new cases in 1967. The epidemics in Nicaragua and Ecuador in the summer of 1967 could be the last to occur in the whole of the two Americas and could be the last in the history of our age, if we put as much total effort in preventing the disease among the present 300 million still unprotected as was relatively placed in Nicaragua to control the epidemic which claimed almost 500 victims. At 8 cents per person for two protecting doses or for $24 million for the hemisphere, this disease could be eradicated in six months by volunteer bands of women and high-

school girls working under the direction of responsible health personnel.

4. Smallpox, which has claimed millions of lives and has wiped out whole cities and nations, including North American Indians, is the one disease, according to Dr. M. G. Candau, the director general of Health of the W.H.O., that can be eradicated forever and completely from the earth. New jet-gun dilution techniques through these high-speed instruments give us the first permanent hope we have ever had of total control of this disease.

5. Measles could be similarly eliminated in five years of intensive effort, with major responsibility of the manufacturing drug and pharmaceutical houses.

6. Though pneumonia and respiratory diseases continue to respond to antibiotics, the increasing use of cigarettes and the increase of diseases due to smoking are wiping out the gains and holding down man's possible longevity faster than medical science can add the possibility of extra years.

The encouraging thing is that health authorities of all the world—regardless of their country's political ideology and the religious culture of their people—are allies in this battle against disease.

# XIV. The Role of
##       Volunteer Agencies

Dr. Hingson is happy about what government is doing. The ambitious, well-financed programs being attempted by the World Health Organization and the U.S. Agency for International Development are essential if we are to meet the emergency health needs of a very sick world.

But the work of governments, with their necessary military-type precision, can deal only with the eradication of disease and the improvement of the physical properties that provide better (and essential) hygiene. This is, at the best, a temporary stop-gap.

Long-range health goals must be accomplished on a people-to-people basis. People of the developing nations must be motivated to mental happiness and personal ambition.

Let me illustrate from an experience on my first trip to a South American capital. I had flown from New York in only a matter of hours, and the thing that sociologists call "cultural shock" hit me stronger than I had imagined. All Saturday afternoon and evening I watched dirty, half-clothed children play in the horse dung and the spoiled fruit that lay in street gutters. Adults were similarly listless and a sense of poverty and hopelessness seemed to characterize the slum area near my hotel.

On Sunday morning, however, I went to a downtown church. The worshipers were well dressed, not expensively but clean. Children were clean, their eyes eager and full of hope. Sunday evening I noticed the same type of happiness at a suburban church. When the last prayer was said, I asked a missionary, somewhat caustically, why his churches ministered only to the well-to-do folk to the neglect of street urchins who needed help so badly.

The missionary was kindly tolerant of my accusation. He smiled and said, "These children here tonight were children of the street only a few months ago. We people in the church reached out to their families and introduced them to faith in a personal God. We told them that we loved them, that God loved them, and that they are important in God's eyes. A new hope was born in their minds and hearts. Fathers who had no jobs went out and found work. Mothers cleaned their houses and washed the family clothes. The children started to our church school."

My doubt was apparent, for he went on: "Yes, this is what the story of Christ's love and God's emphasis on human dignity can mean to any people."

Dr. Hingson recognizes this emphasis on human dignity and personal concern as a kind of health—of continuing hope—that predicts a healthy world tomorrow. And this hope is best motivated through people-to-people programs. I cannot forget the statement of the mayor of Granada, expressing deep appreciation for "people like you who blend your sweat with our sweat to build a better nation."

Dr. Hingson's convincing lectures and written reports following the 1958 Baptist World Alliance survey set the ball in motion for accomplishment of much of this people-to-people effort. Hundreds of volunteer organizations have been established, with the meeting of human need as their goal. Many of these have been religiously motivated. Others have the spark of human kindness—trained men and women contributing of their skills in this country and overseas for the alleviation of human suffering, and for the launching of self-help projects that will eventually meet the total need.

Project HOPE and medical-aid program MEDICO were established in late 1958, in the very wake of the B.W.A. survey trip. Many other such organizations were organized in the years immediately following.

President Kennedy caught a gleam of this same inspiration in his establishment of the Peace Corps. President Eisenhower had already made popular the idea of "people-to-people" projects for world betterment. And President Johnson further spurred the concept with the statement that "People-to-People works outside government in a field vital to us all—the promotion of friendship among the peoples of every land."

Governments had already set a pattern for international cooperation in their United Nations projects and in the World Health Organization. But the people-to-people relationship through volunteer organizations has added a dimension that government can never accomplish by itself.

Bernard Aabel, director of the Department of International Health, American Medical Association (which department was established as a result of Dr. Cleland's recommendation following the 1958 survey), reports that United States organizations are supporting between 600 and 700 health projects in 113 countries. His department also lists 77 organizations which are interested in the distribution of medical material overseas. These figures indicate the sweep of the volunteer spirit—the extent of American compassion for the welfare of the world's peoples. None of these agencies are in business for profit; their motivation is simply the concept of service to their fellow men.

In addition to these figures for volunteer groups, we must remember also the thousands of medical missionaries bringing both physical and spiritual healing to wide areas of the world. The Christian Medical Commission of the World Council of Churches reported that as of January 1967 there were 1,238 medical institutions related to Protestant and Orthodox churches in Asia, Africa, Latin America, and the Near East. They are operated by a total of 330 sponsoring organizations and have a total budget of more than $100 million per year. The Catholic Medical Mission Board of New York reports approximately 5,000 medical institutions under Roman Catholic auspices.

Dr. Hingson's obsession is contagious, and people respond almost automatically to his appeals for brotherly concern and the demonstration of brotherly love to all peoples of the world. His addresses to church groups, to college students, to medical and civic groups bring generous response in kind to his appeal.

Brother's Brother was $101,000 in debt at the end of the Costa Rican campaign. Dr. Hingson and Dr. Antes had signed their names to promissory notes for the vaccines and the guns, and the expected support from foundations failed to come through. So these doctors and other friends have made their appeal to all groups to whom they have spoken; and Dr. Hingson wrote at the end of 1967 that smaller contributions were coming in at the rate of $200 a day. For example, a widow contributed her engagement diamond; a dentist sent $300; the students of State University College at Fredonia, N.Y., gave up their lunch for a day, contributed $695—at $1 apiece—and organized the first Brother's

Brother college chapter. As of this writing, the debt
has been reduced to about $80,000.

Dr. Hingson's basic appeal, however, is not for
money but for volunteers who can share their love
with others on the brother-to-brother basis. Speaking
to the Calvary Baptist Church at Washington, D.C.,
one Sunday in April 1967, he told the Brother's Brother story in simple but compelling language. He explained how God had led in invention of the jet gun,
how God had pointed him to the vaccine dilution
technique, and how God had been glorified in Brother's Brother projects.

He reminded his listeners of their obligation to their
neighbors, and invited those who were interested to
meet him at the church again at 3 P.M.

More than 300 persons came back for the Sunday
afternoon meeting, to learn more about Brother's
Brother and offer their service.

Dr. Hingson tells the volunteers frankly that their
projects will not be a vacation. They will sleep on dirt
floors. They will eat the food of the nationals. They
will almost certainly have intestinal upsets and possibly other illnesses. Their work day will begin at 6 A.M.
and continue often past dark in the evening.

Another requirement: every volunteer is asked to
pay his own way. The rule is an economic necessity
because Brother's Brother uses every contributed dollar to buy guns and vaccines. The rule also serves to
weed out all but the most sincere.

His call is for doctors, nurses, medical students,
medical technicians. But he also asks for youthful volunteers—young men and women of upper high-school
and college age who are willing to run errands on the
field, to scrub equipment, to do anything that may be
required of them. They may be pumping a jet gun be-

fore many days on the field, because the principle of
operation is simple. But there is never any promise of
glamour when Brother's Brother makes its appeal.

Yet, Brother's Brother trustees have a list of 300 to
400 volunteers ready to go on any given summer project. And Dr. Hingson has yet to hear from any who
were disappointed.

Mrs. Ann Probst, a mother and registered nurse of
Lakewood, Ohio, wrote Dr. Hingson of her own reaction to a month of work in Costa Rica, August 1967:

> I can't remember anything in my life that has given me
> more spiritual satisfaction. Indeed I have never worked
> before for four straight weeks without a day off, nor
> have I ever put in longer days than I did up in Guana-
> caste—some of them from 4:30 A.M. to 10:30 P.M.—but
> by the same token never in my life have I wakened to
> such clear fresh mornings where one had the feeling of
> the adventure of doing something worthwhile and useful.
> Let me tell you an experience I had, one of several
> which I shall never forget as long as I live.
> It was while we were in Guanacaste, way out in the
> wilds, I got permission to help out in the pediatric ward
> of the local hospital after we had finished our daily
> vaccinating schedule. It was about 10:30 P.M. the first
> night I got there, and what a shock I got. In one small
> room there were five beds, in these five beds were nine
> children who not only were mixed sexes but mixed dis-
> eases! In another room with eight beds slept thirteen
> children. There was a boy with malaria, who had no net-
> ting or protection of any kind from the mosquitoes which
> were flying in the open unscreened windows. Next to
> him was a boy with 1st, 2nd and 3rd degree burns, ex-
> posed to the air but also to the many flies which were
> swarming around his exposed body which smelled so
> bad. In the next bed was a girl covered from her shaved
> head to her feet with impetigo.
> I worked there for the three nights we were in Guana-

caste, just feeding babies, making beds and changing wet bottoms, between the hours of 10:30 P.M. and 1:30 A.M. On my second night there, two children died: one I couldn't understand why, but the other had had measles and had died of encephalitis. This is the one that made such an impression on me, or rather the mother did. She was sitting on a bench outside with three small children. It was about midnight when the doctor went out to tell her that her little girl had died. All she said was; "Another one, I expected it." Then she turned and walked away leading the other ones, no tears, only a look of agonizing grief on her face, no shoes on any of their feet.

Mrs. Probst then concluded her letter with a look to the future: "Next week, my daughter Ava Louise and I both start to learn Spanish in preparation for the next trip to Latin America. I hope that you will call on me again any time the need arises. Next time I will be more valuable due to this experience and some language knowledge."

Such is the story of Brother's Brother—a movement that challenges all persons moved by the love of Christ to give themselves in the welfare of their neighbor, wherever he may be.

## If You Want to Help

Brother's Brother Foundation is a nonprofit, interfaith, and interracial philanthropic organization emphasizing health and educational service.

Trustees of the Foundation invite the support of individuals, churches, industries and philanthropic foundations for the continuance of its world-wide endeavor.

Needs include:

1. Financial contributions for purchase of equip-

ment, vaccines, and the many expenses of international service.

2. Medical books, teaching materials, and office equipment belonging to doctors who are retired or deceased. These items will be forwarded by the Foundation to points of greatest need.

3. The volunteer services of physicians, nurses, medical technicians and other consecrated individuals who are willing to contribute a month or more of time to humanitarian service overseas.

Contributions and inquiries should be directed to:

Robert A. Hingson, M.D., Director

Brother's Brother Foundation

Forbes Avenue and Halket Street

P.O. Box 7375

Pittsburgh, Pennsylvania 15213

# A Look Toward Mañana

## Epilogue

When the first edition of this book was published and then condensed in Reader's Digest, a swell of gratitude, applause, and contributions flooded through the Foundation's mailboxes at Cleveland, and Canton.

Many young people volunteered their services. Physicians and paramedical personnel similarly voiced their desire to join the Brother's Brother team. Pharmaceutical houses indicated their willingness to contribute or sell at cost the urgently needed vaccines. But most surprising of all—in sheer number—was the flow of financial contributions.

There were no really large gifts. Most letters brought five and ten dollar contributions. The Baptist Federation of Canada sent over a year's period three checks totalling $12,000 which had been contributed in special collections. But the majority of the gifts came from people who have retired and were able to reflect on the significance of the Brother's Brother idea, and from young people who hold idealism in their hearts. They generally were people who wanted to do something tangible to meet the needs and the opportunities they saw evidenced in the Brother's Brother story. Many volunteered to serve wherever needed.

One of the most treasured letters was done in labored pencil lettering. It was folded around the ten cent piece, and it said simply and meaningfully:

"Dear Dr. Hingson,

"I read about you. I think you are a neat guy.

"I am 11 years old. I am going to be a doctor or a hippie when I grow up.

"This money isn't much, but I hope it will help buy some medicine. Good luck."

The response came at an apt time. Dr. Hingson, Dr. Helm, Dr. Amoedo, Mr. Robert Miller and Dr. Antes as trustees had committed Brother's Brother Foundation for a debt of $110,000 to meet the emergency needs in Costa Rica's measles epidemic of 1967 (Chapter XII). Brother's Brother leaders had flown to Costa Rica in response to a frantic cable from the Health Minister Alvara Aguilar Peralta and discovered that one of every eleven affected children were losing their lives to the disease. President Trejos had listened to the plan to restore health to the children of the Republic, then had confessed almost tearfully that his country's cupboard was too bare to pay for the vaccine. Dr. Hingson ordered vaccines, guns, and other equipment from the States "on faith" and the measles threat was quelled.

But in the Fall of 1967, the debt hung heavy. All the normal flow of Foundation income would be required simply to make payments. Projects already being planned might have to be cancelled or at least postponed because of the lack of available money. And this was at a time when new calls were coming from Panama, Honduras, and Nicaragua.

Members of the Brother's Brother team stepped up their speaking schedules at church and temple services, on college campuses and religious conventions. They seldom asked for money, but their testimonies brought contributions almost without exception. Dr. Hingson addressed a mountain retreat of 1100 high school girls in Southern Virginia. He closed with the observation that 10 cents—the price of a soft drink—would save a life. And then he sat down.

Miss Rees Watkins, leader of the retreat, rose to her feet and suggested that some of the girls may wish to contribute their snack money to save a life. "Drop it on the front of the platform when this meeting is over, and we'll pick it up later," she said. The silver had to be swept up with a broom. The total contribution was $703.58.

The Costa Rica government in a unique and responsible act of appreciation promised $5,000.

By June 1969—two years after the original commitment—the debt was reduced to $22,000 and Robert Miller, the foundation's financial advisor was confident that the whole amount would be wiped out by the end of the year.

"Dr. Hingson's faith in the concern of American people for their neighbors has been justified," Miller observed. "They have given an average of more than $4,000 a month toward debt retirement for these last 20 months."

## Courage Brings Triumph in 1968

The indebtedness was obviously a restraint against the future programs. Every appeal from needy nations had to be balanced against available resources—and most of these resources were necessarily allocated to debt retirement.

On the other hand, members of the Foundation's trustee board were committed all along to impossible goals. They already had accomplished the impossible in Liberia, in Honduras, in Nicaragua, in Costa Rica. And their accomplishments had come because they dared to do that which they knew had to be done for the world to live in health and happiness.

The year 1968 was therefore a courageous one. When December's page dropped off the calendar, the report showed 900,000 new vaccinations in Costa Rica and another 100,000 each in Honduras and Nicaragua. The major campaign in Costa Rica was achieved through the cooperative effort of Dr. Aguilar's public health forces and Brother's Brother volunteers—adding more general protection to that given during the 1967 measles epidemic. Dr. Aguilar's doctors and nurses were of help also in training health officials and supporting the efforts in neighboring countries.

Possibly the year's most exciting adventure came in Panama, despite the political unrest which prevented the major coast to coast vaccination program originally planned.

Dr. and Mrs. Lewis Abram of Cleveland and Dr. Manuel Angel Cortes Varjas of Costa Rica, volunteered their services to do as much as possible in the face of an impending change of government. For two weeks in late February they instructed Panamanian doctors, nurses, and public health workers at Panama City in the use of jet inoculation guns. They discussed the need for health protection in all of the isthmus' rural areas, and they left a supply of guns and 25,000 doses of vaccine with the public health service to use as opportunity permitted. The vaccine worth $50,000 was a combined gift through BBF from Costa Rica and the Dow Chemical Society, the patient and understanding creditor for two years.

Then Dr. and Mrs. Abrams climbed aboard a small

plane and flew to the mission clinic of Dr. Daniel Gruver, a youthful Baptist doctor giving his time to the Indian people on the San Blas Island off Panama's Caribbean coast. These interesting and colorful tribal people live in a largely communal society and are painfully aware of the fatal nature of childhood disease in the tropics. The death rate of children from measles is above 30 percent since native medicine men seek to cure high fevers by immersing the patients in the river or ocean.

After a few days of instruction and demonstration at the main clinic, Dr. and Mrs. Abram left two peace guns and a supply of 7,000 vaccines with Dr. Gruver to use in the outlying islands. The rest of the story was told in a letter two weeks later, as an epidemic was totally erased from one of the last pure pre-Columbian nations in the hemisphere.

"I am just beginning to catch my breath and wonder at how the measles vaccine came to San Blas," Dr. Gruver wrote to Dr. Abram. He told of one day's experience "skipping from island to island in a small cayuco, getting badly burned by the sun," to make sure that every child was protected. On four other days the Gruver team used a small airplane to reach the more distant islands. "In the mornings we operated, in the afternoons we vaccinated, and in the evenings we had a full clinic."

Then Dr. Gruver wondered:

"No one will ever know how many deaths were prevented and how much suffering avoided by the campaign. But I am very much interested in knowing how you came to be interested in the San Blas people. As much as I'd prayed and pleaded to get measles vaccine here, how did it happen? To everyone involved I want to extend my fullhearted gratitude."

## A Move for Headquarters

The year was a trying one also because Dr. Hingson moved from Case Western Reserve University at Cleveland to a similar post at the University of Pittsburgh. The Pennsylvania institution loaded him with four titles: Professor of Anesthesiology at the School of Medicine, Chief of Anesthesiology at Magee-Women's Hospital, Professor of Public Health Practice in the Graduate School of Public Health and Professor of Anesthesiology in the School of Dental Medicine.

His decision to change locations was difficult. He had been at Western Reserve for 18 years, and his staff of doctors had provided anesthesia to more than 500,000 patients in seven hospitals. During the last six years, more than 25,000 mothers had been delivered under anaesthesia without mishap.

Pittsburgh offered new opportunities however as the university requested his services in the area of public health as well as anesthesia. So on June 1, 1968, Dr. Hingson moved to the booming steel town. And with him, the offices of Brother's Brother also were transferred to a Pittsburgh address.

Before he left the Cleveland offices, Dr. Hingson paid special tribute to two ladies who had worked diligently—often on their own time—to forward the Brother's Brother ideals.

He said in a memorandum of gratitude mailed to all members of the Foundation:

'It would be impossible to project the life-saving achievements of the Brother's Brother team through the involvement of American resources and sacrificial gifts from individuals, churches and temples of all faiths, without the indefatigable dedication and efforts of the senior secretary, 83-year-old Mrs. Leona Peck and her office partner, Miss Marjorie Fraser. These two women typed,

mailed and composed many of the 50,000 letters required
to initiate this movement of compassion."

Despite her years, Mrs. Peck had joined the Costa
Rican expedition of the team in 1967 in her first air
and overseas flight to a foreign nation. When invited
to participate she immediately responded with scarcely any evidence of surprise, saying: "I always said I
would never fly unless it were a matter of life and
death—but I suppose this is it."

In Costa Rica she walked more than a mile a day in
8,000 foot altitude for breakfast, but as a devout Sev-
enth-day Adventist she maintained her meat-free diet
by boiling eggs to supplement the native fruits and
vegetables for the other two meals.

Mrs. Peck's inordinate involvement motivated her
moving to Pittsburgh for four months to train the new
secretary Miss Sandra Henick to accurately record,
document and transcribe letters which are blueprints
for life saving around the earth.

## A Hope Awaiting Realization in Israel

Dr. Hingson lectured at the Hadassah-Hebrew University Medical Center in Jerusalem in September
1968 at the invitation of Israeli authorities and Hadassah, the Jewish philanthropic organization in the United States. In Israel, he conferred with health authorities about the welfare of an estimated one million
Arab people living in the wide strip of land occupied
by Israel in the June 1967 war.

He learned that these Arab families were largely
without the protection of preventive vaccines. He discovered further that political tension was so great that
the Arab people in this occupied territory were not receptive to medical offers from Israel's public health

workers. Israeli medical men told him that the incidence of communicable disease was rapidly rising among the refugees.

"Can you help us?" asked Dr. J. Yofe, Israel's director general of epidemiology.

Brother's Brother trustees heard the appeal with great interest when Dr. Hingson returned to Pittsburgh. Yes they wanted to help—for here was an opportunity not only to fill a great health gap but to demonstrate the real interfaith meaning of "Brother's Brother" in the tense Middle East. It provided a plan to seek the cooperation of Arab doctors, and to move a team of medical men—one-third from Israel, one-third from Arab territory, and one-third of them Americans from Brothers' Brother—into the area to immunize an estimated 200,000 young children against prevalent diseases. Dow Chemical Company offered to contribute vaccines, and Hadassah, New York, offered to provide $50,000 in cash for transportation and jet gun inoculators.

Dr. Hingson wrote of his plans to Kenneth R. Ziebell, a representative of the World Council of Churches in Jerusalem

"On two weeks notice our Foundation stands ready to extend support toward the control of diseases in the Middle East, within Israel or within any of the neighboring countries. We hope the day will soon arrive when our resources could be pooled through non-political channels yet at the same time in full coordination with responsible health ministries to totally eradicate all of the epidemic diseases in the area—particularly among the poor. It is my belief that with proper planning, coordination, and effort by all of us, poliomyelitis, measles, German measles, tuberculosis, leprosy, diphtheria, typhoid fever, and cholera could be essentially eradicated within three months. Such a plan would save from death 100,000 per year in the Middle East and from diseases, several million. The economy of the area would be definitely improved."

February-March 1969 was set as the target date. The plans had to be indefinitely postponed however when a terrorist bomb exploded in Jerusalem in January 1969 and new tensions diminished to almost nothing, the lines of communication between Jewish and Arab doctors. The plan still is being kept alive, and Brother's Brother hopes for fulfillment of the dream at the earliest possible date.

During Dr. Hingson's September survey, he was conducted through the Garden of Gethsemane by two young guides—a Jewish boy about 11 and an Arab boy of 10. Each of the lads conveyed warmth, friendliness, and respect for the doctor who represented still a third religion. Later at sunset, from the summit of the Mount of Olives above the garden overlooking the entire walled city of Jerusalem, Dr. Hingson wrote this poem in contemplation of the earnest desire of the followers of three great religions—Jewish, Christian and Muslim—to find truth.

## THE THREE UNDERSTANDINGS

### By Robert A. Hingson

Jehovah, God of Israel, Abraham, Isaac, and Ishmael,
God of matchless love and creative power;
Builder of an eternity from years and hours:
Behold all Thy children in permanent strife,
Yet seeking Thee always in birth, death, life,
In confusion, famine, poverty, disease,
Or through happier days between crises.

God of Moses, Mohammed, Isaiah,
Make plain to all man's need of Messiah.

Some Him receive and some Him still expect;
Some Him believed and some still Him reject.

From the prison of Zion, Thy Holy City,
Even John the Baptist echoed man's query:
"Master, are You the One whom God appointed,
Or seek we yet another as God's anointed."

In earnest search we are divided;
Over Jerusalem's traditions we are disunited.
Close to the truth, we fight in disagreement
Or we arm and abet the malcontentment.

Arab and Jewish bullets pierce Bethlehem's sky
And defile the stars as brothers die,
While Christians on the Jericho Road pass by
And hasten to Vietnam, our Armageddon.

God of peace and God of love,
All religions still seek Thy throne above,
To worship Thee and share our brother's home;
Our planet of beauty and bounty rolls,
The bells of the temple, church, and cathedral toll.
While waiting for Your divine plan
May we remember our nationality is Man.

The poem was dedicated to Dr. and Mrs. Blanchard
Antes, the Canton, Ohio, doctor and his wife who
have given so many hours in sacrificial search for scientific and theological truth and for the health of their
fellowmen.

## Future Planning in Central America

Health ministers of the six Central American Republics, reaching from Guatemala to Panama, met in
San Jose, Costa Rica, in June 1969 to plan for future
health plans encompassing the full isthmus area. Dr.
Juan Allwood-Paredes of Salvador, executive secretary
general of the Central American Health Council, and

Dr. Jose Antonio Peraza of Honduras, president of the
Council, invited Dr. Hingson to come to the sessions
and bring a health plan for their consideration.

A large bar graph exhibit greeted the ministers and
their staffs to tell the victorious story of the eradication of measles from Costa Rica. There had been 1,950
reported hospitalized cases of measles in Costa Rica in
1965, 1,439 in 1966, and 3,811 in the epidemic year of
1967. It is generally conceded that the actual number
of cases range from four to ten times this number. But
the number dropped to 97 in 1968—graphic evidence of
the efficiency of the *pistola de la paz* technique and the
Brother's Brother partnership program with Costa Rica
in August 1967.

Dr. Aguilar's staff estimated further that this tremendous reduction in reported cases reflected the saving of thousands of lives, that hospital costs for treatment of measles had dropped 500,000 Colones ($100,000
U.S.) a year, and that the overall saving to the nation
in general was close to two million colones.

Dr. Hingson and Dr. James Bowes, Medical Director of the Dow Chemical Company, whose Pitman
Moore plant had made the vaccines used in 1967
looked at the exhibit and then walked through the
wards of Hospital de los Ninos in San Jose. The nurse
told them that whereas the hospital had averaged 400
cases of measles per month in 1967, they treated a total
of only 20 cases in all of 1968, and have had only 18
the first six months of 1969. None of the six patients
being treated at the time of the June visit had been
vaccinated in 1967. Five of them had been born since
the crusade, and the other, a girl of six, had somehow
been missed.

The exhibit was so graphic that Dr. Hingson scarcely had to say more to convince the health ministers of
the effectiveness of the Brother's Brother program of

cooperative partnership. They listened carefully when
he rose to speak. Not only did they want the details of
his imaginative program, but some sought more light
on his motivations. "Those of us with whom he has
worked in hard campaigns know of his sincerity," one
of the Latin Americans confided, "but others ask what
is *he* going to make out of it. They do not know and
cannot believe that his whole concern is unselfish and
humanitarian."

So Dr. Hingson began:

"The Brother's Brother Foundation, representing a
significant body of professional friends in the United
States and Canada and including more than 200 physicians, is at your service for health, education, and research. We share a dream, a faith, and a belief in your
future. . . .

"You are our permanent friends, our closest neighbors, our continental partners in the inter-relation of
mutually supplementary agriculture, economic enter-
prise, and social culture."

And he continued:

"The unnecessary loss and crippling of your children because of epidemic diseases and deaths of more
than 100,000 every year, is our loss, and humanity's
loss also. It must stop. It is a tragedy greater than the
recently publicized epidemic of accidental deaths on
the highways of our nations."

He next outlined a ten point program for cooperative endeavor between Central American governments
and the volunteer resources for personnel and medicine
available to the Brother's Brother Foundation.

"The foundations for health are solidly established
for the protection of a total of four million children
against communicable diseases," he continued. "We
need to fortify these foundations with another 25 million doses of vaccines against polio, measles, typhoid,

tuberculosis, leprosy, smallpox, whooping cough, and tetanus. We need to extend our program from the Colombian border on into Mexico through Yucatan to the Istmo Tehuantepec."

He then reminded them of comparative value judgments in today's world. "During the next month," he said, "the technology of the jet age will make it possible for man to land on the moon with a budget 1000 times bigger than the budget required to save your children from the plagues of poverty, malnutrition, epidemics and infant mortality that belong to the Middle Ages."

His program called for an outlay of $2,000,000. The cooperating countries were asked to contribute one fourth of it, $500,000, in cash, supplies and services. He expected Brother's Brother to be able to raise a similar amount from churches and other organizations. The pharmaceutical industry would contribute another $500,000 in drugs and supplies, and requests would go to research foundations and commercial fruit companies in Central America for the final fourth. Brother's Brother would supply trained personnel to supervise local doctors and nurses. He suggested that a time table be established to have a new program beginning somewhere in the area each month Republic by Republic until the full objectives are accomplished. Complete victory would save an estimated $22,000,000 per year on treating measles and its complications alone.

Dr. Aguilar, new president of the Health Council, assured Dr. Hingson at the meeting's end that the various ministers were pleased with the proposal and grateful for it. Some countries, he said, were ready to begin work almost immediately; other countries would need to take the program back to their governments for study. A Commission was established to determine maximum resources and to implement the proposal.

Dr. Hingson spent the next week flying to every capital city in the middle Americas. He talked with the presidents in three countries and with the vice president or other high ranking officials in others to urge favorable reaction to the plan.

Meanwhile El Salvador and Guatemala asked for an immediate start of programs. Dr. Paredes and Ralph Hingson, as interpreter and coordinator, traveled directly from the San Jose meeting to the capitals of these countries to set up schedules.

The Brother's Brother dream of eradicating communicable diseases from the American isthmus appeared close to reality, even as the World Health Organization was extending the program begun by BBF in Liberia in 1962 to all the free countries of Asia and Africa.

"Let us develop a blueprint for health, let us conceive of a perpetual charter for peace and cooperation and friendship," Dr. Hingson pleaded in the San Jose meeting. "Let us build together a light house and with our sons and daughters of this and other generations in noble effort share these lessons of scientific and spiritual achievements with all the earth."

And then he added: "But may we never forget that he who builds without God labors in vain."

On that premise Brother's Brother Foundation through its inter-faith, inter-racial, inter-disciplinary medical and education service outreach shares in that spirit with the family of man.

*Appendixes*

# Immunization Against Disease

Edward Jenner, an English physician, discovered the possibility of vaccination in 1796. Physicians for centuries before him had been intrigued by the observation that if a person survived a contagious disease he was not likely to have it again. They reasoned, correctly, that the human body built up protective immunity and would not fall ill again though exposed to the same disease at a later time.

Dr. Jenner took the idea one step further than any of his predecessors. He noticed that milkmaids who contracted cowpox from the udders of cows never fell victim to the disfiguring, deadly smallpox that ravaged England and many sections of the world. He asked himself if there would be an advantage to provoking mild cases of cowpox in his patients, in the hope that this cowpox might prevent later illness from smallpox.

He tried it, and it worked. Vaccines have been developed for more and more diseases as medical knowledge has widened, and most of this advance has come within the past half century.

The immunization procedure results in such a light form of a disease that the body reacts against it without becoming sick. The immunity acquired from vaccination or from having had the disease is called active immunity. Though it diminishes gradually, it lasts for a long time and sometimes for life.

Practically all infants are born with a passive or temporary immunity against most common diseases, because this is passed on to them by their mother. This does not last long, however, and cannot be depended upon in case of an epidemic.

Here are some of the prevalent diseases for which immunization is possible:

*Smallpox.* This disease, known in many parts of the world as variola, is prevalent in parts of Asia, Africa and Latin America, and a continuing threat to all countries. Jet airplane travel lets it be transmitted great distances. It is characterized by a rash developing into pustules and then scabs, and is fatal in about 30 per cent of cases.

Dr. Jenner's discovery in 1796 is still effective, and injection of vaccine with a jet injector or the long-popular multiple-puncture technique is being practiced in all the more developed countries. Revaccination is advised every three to five years.

*Diphtheria.* Before 1900, diphtheria was among the most dreaded diseases of infants and young children. Experimentally, a German physician injected horses with increasing doses of a toxic fluid in which diphtheria organisms had been grown. He discovered that a protein substance known as antitoxin was produced in the horses' blood. When removed from the blood and injected into persons who were exposed to diphtheria, this antitoxin saved their lives by creating passive immunity.

It was discovered about 1914, however, that children could be actively immunized against diphtheria by injection of minute amounts of the same toxic fluid which produced antitoxin in horses. More recently, a modified form of this substance, called diphtheria toxoid, was developed and is now used for diphtheria immunization. It is usually combined with tetanus toxoid and whooping-cough vaccine for the basic immunization of infants against all three of these diseases. The combination vaccine is known as D.P.T. (for diphtheria, pertussis, and tetanus).

*Whooping cough.* This disease claimed the lives of a great many young children before the early 1930's, when a potent vaccine was perfected. It still causes more deaths among babies than scarlet fever, diphtheria, measles, and polio combined, yet these diseases are much more feared.

Most whooping-cough deaths result from complications which affect the lungs, although the brain sometimes is affected by the severe convulsive coughing.

Protection against whooping cough is acquired by injections of a suspension of killed whopping-cough organisms. Effective immunity develops about a month after the injections are administered.

*Tetanus.* Immunization against tetanus is of growing importance because of the danger of infections in wounds. Tetanus toxoid is usually included in the triple or quadruple vaccines already mentioned or may be injected separately. In case of wounds which could be infected with tetanus organisms, a booster dose of toxoid or passive immunizations through tetanus antitoxin may be advised by the physicians.

*Poliomyelitis.* Of all the diseases that threaten little children, crippling and killing polio is feared most by the majority of parents. After many years of research, a method has been discovered by which the different varieties or strains of the polio virus can be grown artificially. From these cultures were developed two kinds of polio vaccine: the Salk, or killed vaccine, and the Sabin, or live vaccine.

The Salk vaccine is given in a series of injections;

the Sabin vaccine is administered in a series of doses
by mouth on a lump of sugar or in a sweet liquid.

*Measles.* Measles, generally accepted as a "normal"
childhood disease in the United States, has a death
rate as high as one in every ten cases in Latin America,
where children are already weakened by malnutrition.
A human blood derivative, gamma globulin, has been
used to provide milder reaction to the disease. But
now a successful live vaccine has become available,
and a single dose is believed to give lasting immunity.

*Influenza.* Influenza vaccine is advised for anyone
who has chronic heart disease, lung or kidney disease,
diabetes, and generally for people over sixty-five. Immunization should be given in the autumn. The first
vaccination against influenza consists of two doses; an
annual booster dose each autumn is advised subsequently. This vaccine is grown on egg media, so anyone allergic to eggs should not have the vaccine.

*Typhoid fever.* Typhoid germs are transmitted generally through water and food which has been exposed
to the germ in the soil. The illness is prevalent in areas
where proper sanitary facilities are not used for dis-
posal of human wastes. It is unlikely in modern communities where water, milk and food supplies are safe-
guarded by purification or pasteurization. Vaccination,
given in a series of three shots, is needed when one
travels into primitive areas or when catastrophe causes
disruption of food-protection processes.

*Tuberculosis.* Tuberculosis, largely eliminated as a
threat in the more developed countries, still continues
to be a disastrous and killing disease in many parts of
the world. It is estimated that one of every five persons in the tropics is afflicted. A single-shot vaccine
was developed by Calmette and Guérin of France in
the 1920's. It is known as B.C.G. from the names of its
developers.

*Leprosy.* The dread skin disease that cripples and disfigures its victims is one of the historic plagues of mankind. It currently afflicts 10 million people, mostly in tropical areas. In 1960, Dr. J. A. Kinear Brown, a leprosy specialist in Uganda, discovered that the B.C.G. vaccine used for tuberculosis is also effective in the prevention of leprosy. Early tests showed a reduction of 80 per cent occurrence of leprosy in areas where the vaccine is used.

*Cholera.* Cholera continues to make outbreaks in large areas of Asia, despite medical knowledge that it can be prevented by adequate hygiene. The disease is characterized by diarrhea and vomiting, and is fatal unless the fluid loss is replaced. It has no age preference, but mortality rates are highest among the very young and the very old. Several vaccines have been developed, but immunization is of short duration.

*Yellow fever.* Though yellow fever is now rare among humans, it continues to plague monkeys in tropical areas and can be transmitted to humans by mosquitos. The disease was most common, and became best known, because of thousands of yellow-fever deaths among men trying to build the Panama Canal. That epidemic was halted when U. S. Surgeon General Gorgas eliminated or controlled the mosquitoes. A live vaccine, cultivated on hen's eggs, is available, and immunization lasts about ten years.

*Still more developments.* Atomic Eenergy Commission scientists announced in August 1967 the development of an advanced zonal centrifuge which will allow the separation of pure virus from all foreign material in the culture. It is this foreign material, which could not be entirely separated by previous methods, that has sometimes caused disagreeable side effects from vaccination. Possibly even the usual post-vaccination soreness in the arm will be eliminated. In addition to providing purer vaccines, the centrifuge with its speed of 35,000 revolutions per minute will open avenues for further experimentation on new vaccines. Possibly, scientists say, even a cancer vaccine may be developed.

# My Experience
# with the Lord Jesus*

### by Robert A. Hingson, M.D.

In Cleveland, Ohio, in the Maternity building of University Hospitals, Julia, a young Negress, age seventeen, was sweating out the middle third of a tumultuous birth process with her first baby. With clenched fists rhythmically pounding her pillow at the beginning of each two-minute "belly whopper" that propelled the new baby toward the outside world, she fervently chanted a prayer unexcelled in urgent sincerity: "Help me, Jesus! Help me, Doctor! Help me, Jesus! Help me, Doctor!—Jesus, You ain't paying one bit of attention to pore me!" It was my privilege as the doctor in this instance, as a veteran of 16,000 such deliveries during the past quarter of a century, to provide the means, the technique and the medication in bringing about a God-inspired surcease from her suffering by helping a young Jewish physician insert this malleable needle into the very delicate spot that would instantaneously block the processes of pain from the sixteen nerves that carry sensation in labor. I whispered encouragement to the young mother to

* An address to the 1957 Laymen's Leadership Institute, Southern Baptist Theological Institute, Louisville, Kentucky, January 17, 1957.

keep praying, since the help of Jesus would surely
make us of the First Team. The young Jewish doctor,
sweating through his first such anesthetic, whispered
back to me, "This is the first time I was ever on the
same team with Jesus!" Within five minutes the pains
of abdomen, pelvis, back and bottom subsided and absolute physical comfort returned to Julia, through
whose moistened brown eyes shone forth a heartfelt
gratitude as she said, "I wish the Mother of Jesus
could have had some of this medicine."

In the U. S. Marine Hospital on Staten Island, New
York, in 1942, three days after he had been picked up
from the Atlantic as the sole survivor of a submarine
torpedo disaster destroying his merchant ship and
forty-two shipmates, a Mississippi Negro named John,
age forty-six, told me, his physician, his story. He had
been asleep when the explosion came. His first conscious sensation was the closing of a cold wet sea in
the midnight hours over his face. His outstretched
arms engulfed a large log of lumber onto which he
climbed and on which he was tossed for two days and
nights by a moderately turbulent sea before the U. S.
Coast Guard rescue. As I recorded in a medical history
this thrilling personal story, I raised the question of
loneliness during this perilous saga. John replied,
"Doctor, I wasn't lonely. I talked to the Lord Jesus day
and night. Me and Him grew to be pretty good bud-
dies." I asked the question, "Did the Lord Jesus talk to
you?" John replied, "Oh, yessuh! He sent the Coast
Guard after me."

In 1938, I stood beside the deathbed of a courageous old Norwegian merchant captain whom we
called "Texas" because of his hundred crossings of the
Atlantic with oil from Texas to Norway. I felt defeated
as I saw the processes of a painful infiltrating cancer
of the lung come to grips with the life and comfort of

my patient. As a hopeless symbol of defeat I lit the pipe of this old salt as he asked me how many more days he might live. I told him perhaps long enough for me to send a cable to his only survivor, a young merchant-marine son aboard his ship making the Atlantic crossing that would surely bring him to the bedside of his father. Old Texas between smoke rings said, "Doctor, leave him be. I can close my eyes and visualize his every move on the ship I know so well. I must leave with that memory that must not be marred in my world to come by having it compete with one of my grief-stricken lad beside the bedside of this ugly old shipwreck. You stay close to me, Doctor. I need you before I go to God. Good night."

During Birth, during Life, at Death I have almost touched the hand of the Lord Jesus as His love, His concern, His compassion have been extended to each individual who needed Him and His philosophy. I was introduced to Him at my own boyhood fireside, in my own village church, through my Christian friends in a religious America, in my schools, through the Baptist Student Union at the University of Alabama. Through Doctor Luke in his gospel I heard Him say, "to inherit eternal life . . . sell all that thou hast, and distribute unto the poor . . . and come, follow me." [Luke 18:18-22]. During the depression years during my premedical training and while working as an orderly in the University Hospital and after I had sold all my worldly goods—a beloved iron-gray saddle horse and two young cows—I became imbued with the magnificent obsession that real happiness comes only through purpose and dedication in a life of service. For me it was the field of medicine.

When the price of cotton fell to 6 cents a pound in Alabama; when my father lost his health and fortune through the bankruptcy of the farmer creditors; when the University treasurer told me I had only one more week to remain in school because of inability to pay my fees; when the stone wall of frustration seemed insurmountable, my faith in the Biblical contracts of God was tested but never doubted. Under the stars of Tuscaloosa I prayed for help as Julia from Cleveland, John from Mississippi and Texas from Norway had done.

*My prayer then and my prayer now* was one of dedication through the Lord Jesus to the Heavenly Father. I laid hold of the promises of God with the promise that through the career of the physician I would be an instrument in the hand of God to those who suffer, regardless of race or creed or country.

My first uniform was an apron for the purpose of serving tables in the college boarding house. My first surgical instrument was an ordinary mop and a pail of Lysol solution to clean the operating rooms as a hospital orderly. My home for five years was an abandoned and reconstructed miniature-golf house, without heat for the first winter, purchased by a benevolent Baptist minister and friend and dragged down a car track by mules from an open field to hospital property. My teachers were the finest Alabama and Georgia could provide save one: The Great Physician, whose concern for a suffering humanity became my concern.

The degrees, the medical opportunities, the joys and thrills of a full life were compounded upon me: New York; the Mayo Clinic; submarine patrol in the North Atlantic and the North Sea; Jefferson Medical College in Philadelphia; a tempting advancement back in New York (but this was rejected for an appointment among the Negroes in the University of Tennessee in Memphis); an Associate Research Professorship in Johns Hopkins University School of Medicine; and then many offers and the actual conduct of teaching clinics in every North American medical school and most of those west of the Iron Curtain in Europe, and many in South and Central America. But the patients remained the same: those with pain in childbirth, infection with venereal disease, leprosy, the burns of war, the casualties of trauma.

*My second prayer of rededication* came in New York before the birth of our first son, when I sought in vain through the medical literature of the world for sure knowledge to alleviate the pains of birth. The answer came back so unequivocally that already more than 2 million American babies* have arrived safely, and many doctors think more safely than ever before, because of a sixteen-nerve anesthetic technique that spared mother and baby brain from anesthetic poisons. Through evolutionary modifications of this new technique more than 1 million babies each year in America alone cry lustily from their first breath and their mothers smile in the instant of birth, because the orderly plan of God awaits only its proper interpretation and application in harmony with the love revealed to us by the Son of God.

To me this great new field of medicine seemed so big that I almost lost sight selfishly of my own promise to serve God wherever He should direct, as I tangled with the scientific blind alleys of research and with the skeptical physicians' debate. I was jarred back on the path while I researched life's values as a convalescent from a three months' illness which had threatened even life itself. *For the third time I prayed the prayer of rededication* and asked to be used again, not for personal gain or glory, but rather for those who still needed help regardless of geography, race, finances, deprivations or even demotions involved. The answer

* Now 8 million—Author.

was quick in coming: Separate invitations from Colombia, Venezuela, Panama, San Salvador and Mexico
reintroduced me to types of poverty and need almost
vanishing in our prosperous America. Invitations for
three years to teach in the famed Booker T. Washington Tuskegee Institute among the Negroes, in Atlanta's Grady Hospital, among the poor in Cleveland's
City Hospital, reintroduced me to America's number
one internal problem: the need on the part of all her
citizenry to bury for all time racial prejudice by sharing equally God's love with all men. I found that the
challenges of Alabama's Africa and Georgia's Africa
and Cleveland's Africa were just as challenging and
just as rewarding as Schweitzer's Africa and Haiti's
Africa. In all these areas alike we must seek God's
guidance toward solution of these terrific problems.

Sometimes the diamonds and nuggets of life are
more beautiful in the shining reflections of gratitude
from the eyes of those who need us than in the palaces
of the kings. The Lord Jesus has taught me to research
for new truths not in the vineyards of the favored few,
but in the barren ground of the neglected poor—not in
the laboratories or operating rooms of the superscien-
tists but among the lowly, the meek and the humble.

I am convinced that God has no favored nation, no
favored race. We who love God must love all the
world's peoples. And while all people are equal in the
sight of God, they are grossly unequal in health, in
available nutrition, in life expectancy. It is just as imperative for America's affluent people to minister to
the unfortunate in our midst and to the leper in Africa
as it was for the traveler to give aid to the wounded
man in Jesus' story of the Good Samaritan.

With Luke I have marveled at the miracle of the
Christ; with Schweitzer I have followed the quest of
the Historical Jesus, whose influence in my life too has

kindled the "reverence for life." Yet with Julia and
Mississippi John and Norwegian Texas and their
brothers and sisters who suffer, I have felt the challenge of the Lord Jesus. In accepting the challenge
and the Challenger I have given of my life to receive it
back again more abundantly. It is this great experience which I wish to share with this distinguished and
dedicated company.

# The Physician and the Burning of Rome*

by Robert A. Hingson, M.D.

In the first century A.D., a Roman emperor with a callous conscience observed the collapse of the acme of civilization in the burning of the Eternal City. Historians record that Nero fiddled as the flames consumed Rome.

During 1958, in a 45,000-mile journey, a peri-global survey of medical missions and national hospitals of many faiths and sects was completed. Our team of sixteen specialists in medicine, nursing, and nutrition, with hospital supply executives, paused in thirty-two countries of the outer rim of Asia and Africa to observe and record, and in some instances to render medical treatment. We found a world in which more than one-third of its occupants were being destroyed by the flames of disease. We knew that the world was sick— but it was much sicker than we thought!

As we, representing the specialties of Anesthesia, Medicine, Obstetrics and Gynecology, Pediatrics, Public Health, and Surgery, examined the hospitals, clinics, public health stations, and schools manned by the thousands of selfless and dedicated missionaries as our

* Reprinted, with slight editing, from *American Practitioner and Digest of Treatment*, Vol. 10, No. 10, October, 1959.

most tangible and consistent examples of concern for our neighbors, we came face to face with mankind's greatest enemy: Disease. We observed its vectors, its tragic onslaught upon the economy of many nations, and its devastating and paralyzing effects upon men of all races. We who had observed the effects of World War II at close range became convinced that war ranks a poor third behind famine and disease in its destructive force.

After conferences with ministers of health and goverment officials in each of these nations; after study of the health statistical reports of each; after seeing the patients in the overpopulated city slums, in the villages, in the jungles and in the bush of these countries of more than 2 billion human beings; after immunizing 90,000 of them by American gift vaccines against poliomyelitis, cholera, or typhoid, we tabulated and estimated the disease problem in these nations. The ten major diseases as we found them were:

|  | 1958 | 1968 |
|---|---|---|
| 1. Malaria .......... | 200,000,000 | 100,000,000 |
| 2. Tuberculosis ...... | 75,000,000 | 50,000,000 |
| 3. Malnutrition, including severe anemia, kwashiorkor, starvation ............. | 50,000,000 | 150,000,000 |
| 4. Intestinal diseases of cholera, typhoid, paratyphoid, and dysentery caused by bacterial flora and amoebae .. | 50,000,000 | 30,000,000 |
| 5. Intestinal parasites, amoebae and worms | 150,000,000 | 150,000,000 |
| 6. Trachoma, affliction of eyes ............. | 50,000,000 | 40,000,000 |
| 7. Bilharzia or snail | | |

| | | |
|---|---|---|
| disease ........... | 50,000,000* | 250,000,000 |
| 8. Infectious diseases of the skin, yaws, jungle rot, smallpox and measles ........... | 50,000,000 | 25,000,000 |
| 9. Severe mental apathy inconsistent with self-sustenance ........ | 25,000,000 | 25,000,000 |
| 10. Leprosy .......... | 20,000,000 | 10,000,000 |
| 11. Smallpox .......... | 150,000,000 | 65,000 |

One of our surgeons remarked to the writer after participating in this experience: "To consider one of the world's major health needs as surgery would be the same as fiddling while Rome burns." Indeed, in these days when many plans are being proposed by statesmen, physicians with limited experience in only one or two countries, neophytes of problems of monsoon, jungle and desert, specialists who plug a hobby, and "textbook specialists" in disease and international politics, we are getting ahead of reason in translating our emotions into action.

First there is a need for fact-finding surveys in bilateral concert with the agricultural, educational, medical, engineering, sociologic and political leaders of the indigenous peoples toward whom we are directing our assistance. Only then can we tie man's resources intelligently to man's need in an acceptable form. Educational assistance can be offered when we are ready to carry through a continuing plan. The exchange students now in most of these countries and our country can pave the way.

The physician who has rendered such a creditable

---

* Better methods of detection and epidemiology are identifying more cases and confirming that 40 per cent of Africans have this disease.

service in making America the healthiest nation in the world has much to share through coordinated effort, but he has much to learn too. Our medical schools which have geared their training to combating the diseases of our prosperous country, to Main Street, U.S.A., can learn too through sending members of their faculties in rotation to assist in neighboring, friendly, and receptive underdeveloped countries. Teams of medical students in their free elective quarter, and young physicians in training, can be taught the principles of vaccination and immunization, and loaned to a specific area in which there has been prearranged transportation, sustenance and supervision and planned direction. Such would be a rewarding experience for the medical student, the physician in training and the responsible medical faculty as well. Such experience would enrich the institution and personnel who sponsor it toward becoming important factors in a world community. This loan of personnel could be effectively correlated with the splendid lifesaving gifts of supplies and food through our national philanthropy of CARE and our Christian medical mission programs.

The medical society at the county, state, regional and national levels within the framework of the American Medical Association and World Medical Association, and within the framework of each specialty, has a definite responsibility, a challenge and an opportunity toward the alleviation of the world's suffering and in making the most meaningful contributions toward world peace. As a start each local county medical and dental society could adopt one single medical mission and supply it with continuing provisions of medical texts, instruments and drugs. The immensity of the task should not ensnarl us in the whirlpool of attempting too much through dispersion of our efforts too far, too soon. There are 2 billion people in Asia and Africa alone or more than ten people in urgent need for every single person in the United States. The majority of these people are under the domination economically or politically of "enlightened" European powers. As America tackles the problems of the world in such projects as the "Great White Fleet" of moth-ball hospital ships privately manned, in people-to-people programs, with the "Medico," with the foundations, and with denominational missions (even though each of these is important in long-range ultimate objectives), there should be established first certain priorities and proving grounds and "trial flights" for mastering the same lessons that have been learned at Cape Canaveral, in the World Health Organization, in the United Nations, and in the historic contacts with the recipient nations themselves.

As we preach democracy and salvation we should keep our eyes on the fundamental health needs of Asia and Africa (all beginning with the letter S): (1) Sanitation, (2) Sewers, (3) Sprays, (4) Screens, (5) Schools, (6) Soup, (7) Shots, (8) Shoes, (9) Self-respect, and then only (10) Salvation. Indeed, the needs of the world are primarily public health and nutrition.

The development and application of the Salk vaccine has taught us the lesson that with all of our propaganda, all of our medical and scientific knowledge and skill of our physicians, we have protected only less than one-half of our population. Our needles, syringes, sterilization, transportation processes, and available personnel were simply not enough to tackle the social impediments of our well-organized America. Twenty-six preparation minutes per injection through this approach has not eliminated poliomyelitis in America, now in its worst outbreak in six years,* nor will it

* As of 1958—Author.

eliminate the millions of other pestilences which beset the world. For the past two decades the author of this editorial has developed the principle of jet inoculation, and now adapting the repeat jet principle from immense reservoirs we proved, in inoculating 41,000 children and employees of the U. S. Post Office in Cleveland, and 90,000 on our world journey within a space of four months, that we can deliver one immunizing injection each six seconds without resterilization. Sabin oral vaccine now points the way to total control in the developing nations.

It will take such total mobilization of planned effort and mass volunteer teams of indoctrinated physicians who will donate their time to join other concerned Americans and world citizens of many nations and of all religious faiths who can provide transportation, equipment, diplomatic international contacts, education and simultaneous agricultural and engineering assistance; to make lasting contributions in the vital field of world health and world peace. To dissipate effort in tackling all the world's problems at once, in competition and out of step with the British and the French and the Belgians and the Dutch and the Russians, would be the equivalent of "fiddling while Rome burns."

Public Health, Improved Nutrition, and Education are the basic needs which must be supplied before the medical specialties of Surgery, Radiology, Anesthesia, Pathology and Physical Therapy can be intelligently and effectively developed in these countries. Never before has the welfare of six continents presented itself before such a capable and scientific medical profession with such a limited time table. We, the physicians, can and must extinguish the flames of mass disease and suffering in the vanguard of civilization's most promising era.

APPENDIX  *4*

# The Solution

Dr. Hingson has proposed the following steps in solution of world health problems:

1.  Develop and implement a logistical plan to eradicate continent by continent the diseases of major significance responding to mass immunization.

2.  Immediately allocate budget needs for eradication of each disease, such as smallpox, measles and poliomyelitis, into new resource pools for concentration on the next major controllable disease.

3.  Search for, develop, and project interdenominational cooperation in medical missions, such as exemplified by Vellore Medical Center in India and the Evangelical Medical Center at Kimpese, Congo. On the basis of Christian service develop a pilot lighthouse center with Catholics, in areas where maximum Communist pressure is being exerted, to demonstrate unity of Christians. A common cooperation by teams of Arabs and Jews in uniting to combat health menaces would electrify the world and inspire other warring segments.

4.  Emphasize to all future medical missionaries and planning boards the increasing value of public health in reaching the masses through medical missions. Comparably, the return yield in lifesaving from public

health will be at least tenfold greater than from expensive hospital, medical and surgical care.

5. Increase the period of training of each medical missionary prior to assignment, through at least two years of approved residency training beyond internship, with an additional six months to be spent in public health graduate programs such as the one conducted by the Harvard Medical School, and/or the one offered by the U. S. Navy Medical Research Institute on Tropical Diseases in Cairo, Egypt, in the NAMRU Center.

6. Institute and develop elective externships as orientation for full-time and part-time medical mission work, to be offered by such missionary general hospitals as: Kyoto Baptist Hospital in Japan; Severance Medical School and Hospital in Seoul, Korea; Baptist Wallace Mission Hospital in Pusan, Korea, in cooperation with other denominational hospitals of that city; Iloilo Mission Hospital in the Philippines; Baptist Mission Hospital in Moulmein, Burma; and the Kimpese, Congo, medical center; with deans of American medical schools assigning junior and senior medical students, for their elective one to two quarters of their medical training. Already some of our medical schools are letting students select institutions in any country in which they would like to explore their special interest. The Smith, Kline & French pharmaceutical company has in the past decade developed 246 such fellowship awards.

7. Develop laymen's committees for receiving contributions that may be made by laymen in America—and in the developed countries.

   a. Solicit and distribute gifts of money and material.

   b. Establish information center, with secretarial help, that will write to widows of recently deceased doctors (announced in the *Journal of the American*

*Medical Association*) who would be willing to give
part or all of libraries, medical instruments and drugs
to medical missions.

*c.* Establish organizational channels in churches to
collect and transship medical libraries, useful medicines and free samples.

*d.* Approach drug companies for specific gifts of
surplus or best price purchase.

*e.* Approach governmental agencies for distribution
of surplus and AID material to needed areas through
interfaith missions.

8. Establish—to cooperate with and implement established health agencies:

*a.* Voluntary pools of doctors from general practice and from subspecialties, who could give three to
six months of their time with aid without transportation being furnished, to medical missions, such as re-
placement of sick or deceased personnel, during furlough time, and during periods of disaster or increased
responsibility.

*b.* Voluntary pools of teachers and educators who
would teach in both missionary and national elementary and secondary schools and universities, for a se-
mester or one or two years. Officials in Egypt, Iran,
India and the Philippines requested this type of help.

*c.* Voluntary pools of agricultural professionals to
study and develop, through missions and national governments, ways and means of increasing and improv-
ing food supply.

*d.* Voluntary pools of nurses, nutritionists and die-
titians.

*e.* Voluntary pools of engineers.

*f.* Consultants in metallurgy and mineralogy.

*g.* Voluntary pools of dentists.

9. Develop interracial cooperation in America
among large population groups of white and Negro,

Indian and mixed groups such as Puerto Ricans and Mexicans, who would demonstrate unity of faith, purpose and cooperation, to countries receiving the greatest benefit and exhibiting greatest need, in Asia, Africa and South America.

10.  Change the concept and the modus operandi of "Brother's Keeper" to Brother's Brother in all future service projects in the United States, with interracial cooperation projected therefrom across the six continents.

11.  Develop broad imaginative plans and logistical dispersion in partnership with the afflicted nations across areas and whole nations in epidemics in crises of the world's abundant resources toward supplying desperate human needs.

12.  The narrow Central American corridor of seven important nations is the most economical and deserving segment of the world's population for pilot lighthouse eradication of disease as proving ground for these theories. Our foundation work there during the past three years, wherein we have reached 3 million, confirms this thesis. At least we have begun. At least we must continue.

13. Practice and project the second great commandment: *Thou shalt love thy neighbor as thyself.*

*"Hands of human mercy are not unlike the Hands of God."*